2 00

New Voices of Hispanic America

New Voices of Hispanic America

An Anthology

Edited, translated and with an introduction

by Darwin J. Flakoll and Claribel Alegría

Beacon Press   Boston

1962

To our children
Maya, Patricia, Karen, Erik

PREFACE

We had hoped, during the preparation of this anthology, that the poems and short stories by a new generation of writers from Hispanic America would provide the public living beyond the borders of that region with a keener awareness of its vastness, its jungles, rivers and mountains and, above all, with an insight into its people and culture. Gradually we came to realize that—despite differences in historical background, in scenery or environment, in quirks of temperament—the writers who speak to you from these pages are not strangers. They are not foreign or exotic, but recognizable human beings struggling with familiar problems and undergoing universal experiences.

Leading critics, editors of literary magazines, writers and professors of Latin American literature were asked to name their choices for inclusion in this volume; the nominees were then requested to submit their books or manuscripts for study and to suggest further nominations from their own generation. Anthologies and prizewinning stories from literary competitions were studied carefully; announcements in Latin-American newspapers and literary magazines threw open the doors to any young writer who wished to compete. Our apologies are due the hundreds of talented young writers who, for reasons of space or because their existence was unknown to us, must be excluded from this anthology.

Selection was restricted to the Spanish-speaking countries of Latin America and to those writers born in 1914 or later. This was an arbitrary delimitation, reached partly in an effort to avoid overlapping the scope of existing anthologies and partly as a compromise answer to the question, How old can a new writer be?

Obviously, a volume of this size cannot claim to be an exhaustive collection of contemporary Hispanic-American literature. The sheer quantity of the literary output and immense geographical area in which it has been created prohibit any such consideration. Think of this, then, as a literary showcase, in which are displayed—many for the first time to a non-Spanish-speaking audience—samples of the new creative literary talents from "south of the border."

The reconstruction method of translation generally was discarded in favor of a more nearly literal rendition, except where basic differences between the two languages forced modification in the interest of clarity. Poetic selections were restricted almost entirely to free verse, eliminating formal structures—such as the sonnet—which become ineffective when released from their disciplining framework. Regretfully, too, many excellent poems could not be used because their charm, which is based on musical qualities inherent in the Spanish language, was not susceptible to a rendering into English.

We wish to thank all those who helped to guide us through the vast labyrinth of writing which encompasses the nineteen Spanish-speaking countries of Latin America.

This book was made possible through the generosity and patience of The Catherwood Foundation, Bryn Mawr, Pennsylvania, during the period of its gestation (1954-1956) and particularly through that of its president, Mr. Cummins Catherwood.

Special thanks are due Dr. Arnold Chapman, of the University of California's Department of Spanish and Portuguese, for his invaluable help and criticism. Grateful acknowledgment for advice and assistance is extended to the following, among many others: Francisco Giner de los Ríos, Oscar Acosta, Joaquín García Monge, Mario Espinosa Wellman, Mariano Picón Salas, Darío Carmona, María Luz Montané, Enrique Espinoza, Emir Rodríguez Monegal, Juan Ramón Jiménez, Cristobal Garcés Larrea, Juan Rejano, Mauleón Castillo, Alberto Baeza Flores, Dolores Castro, Luís Alberto Sánchez and Padre Alfonso Escudero.

DARWIN J. FLAKOLL
CLARIBEL ALEGRÍA

Contents

INTRODUCTION

At first glance an international boundary seems to be an abstract concept, an arbitrary but purely imaginary line. If the boundary happens to be the one between the United States and Mexico, for example, you will find on either side the same sort of buildings set on a brown plain under the same implacable sun. The differences begin to register gradually as one rolls southward across the desert. The superficial contrasts of language, architecture, standards of comfort, food, can be absorbed rapidly by the hurrying tourist. But there is a remnant, an undefinable something that cannot be neatly categorized and filed away in the mind. It is a tempo, a style, a grave reserve in the face of Indian or Spanish *hidalgo* alike, an empathy that goes beyond the difference of language. The sense of something alien, vaguely disturbing or exciting, remains even when one lunches on a hot dog and Coca Cola at Sanborn's soda fountain or flees into an airconditioned theater on Avenida Madero to see a Hollywood spectacular. Mexico— Latin America as a whole—refuses to be, cannot be, Main Street.

The Spanish-speaking countries of Latin America sprawl along 87 degrees of latitude from the Rio Grande southward to Cape Horn. Eighteen republics and one associated state, which share a common tongue, are tossed like a partly assembled jigsaw puzzle on a rumpled bed. Every imaginable kind of geography and climate is to be found somewhere in Hispanic America, and dramatic contrasts frequently are set side by side.

The Mexico City–Cuernavaca freeway winds through

a barren upland abandoned to cactus, brown grass and tilted lava blocks. There is one point on this desert highway where the snow-covered peaks of Popocatepetl and Ixtacihuatl (the Sleeping Woman) come into view while the rank tropical vegetation of Cuernavaca is still visible several thousand feet below.

In southern Chile the western slope of the Andes is bathed by moisture-laden Antarctic winds that nourish an exuberant sub-arctic rain-forest vegetation and imposing glaciers. A few miles east the Argentine side of the *cordillera* is parched and dry. Farther north in Chile, the Atacama Desert and the western slope of the Andes never know rain, because the west wind dumps its moisture over the cold Humboldt Current several hundred miles at sea. On the eastern side of the narrow range, the jungles of eastern Peru and lowland Bolivia are battered by constant rains that drain off to become the world's largest river: the Amazon.

Simón Bolívar liberated the continent from Spanish rule and dreamed of a United States of Latin America. His dream was thwarted by human pettiness and perversity to some extent, but his real enemies were the mountains, jungles, deserts and plains, the enormous distances that made centralized government a physical impossibility.

Instead, the breaking up of Spain's New World empire created a titanic laboratory where, in a flight of whimsy, one might imagine some cosmic scientist introducing variables of geography, climate, resources and racial intermixture into nineteen separate experiments to determine their end effect on the subject: the Spanish stock which brought to the New World almost five hundred years ago a language, a culture, a religion and a pioneer determination to bend nature to its will.

To stretch fantasy one notch further, one might imagine the same experimenter setting up a second control project in North America approximately one hundred years later. In this series a more varied stock of North European peoples founded thirteen colonies that broke away from the mother country almost half a century before the Spanish colonies won their independence. Faced with less rigorous geographic and climatic problems, these people achieved a hard-won political unity and pursued their own distinctive line of cultural and political development.

The present-day contrast between the two Americas is deeply rooted. It cannot be explained away entirely by pointing out differences in geography, climate or political cohesiveness. Something more remains: an elusive compound of temperament, historical experience, cultural imprint and social nuance. These are subtle things, but they contribute as much as the material factors to the jolting contrasts between North American and Latin-American standards of value and ways of life.

The question of race, to take one example, has entirely different dimensions in Latin America than it has in the United States. Settlers in North America discovered only a sparse indigenous population in an early stage of agricultural and fishing production. Farther west, on the Great Plains, the Indians were still more backward, possessing only a nomadic hunting culture. The resulting encounter was cruel but predictable: the Indians were decimated if they resisted being pushed back to the fringes of the settled area, and eventually the few survivors were left to eke out a subsistence on the least desirable lands.

In Latin America, on the other hand, Hernan Cortés and Francisco Pizarro encountered highly cultured, flourishing civilizations. Agriculture was sufficiently advanced to permit the valley of Mexico, Central America and Peru to support teeming populations. The Spanish *conquistadores*

were few in proportion to the native population. Unlike
the North American settlers, who generally brought their
families with them, the Spaniards were usually unmarried
adventurers anxious to wrest quick wealth from the New
World and then return to Spain. The solution here was
also predictable. The Spaniards conquered by liquidating
the small ruling clique of pagan priests and princes and
usurping the latter's place at the top of the social pyramid.
They married or took Indian concubines and begot mestizo
children. And thus, casually, they set the caste pattern that
was to endure throughout most of the continent into the
twentieth century: a small elite class, usually of pure Spanish blood, which owned nearly all the land; a larger group
of mixed, mestizo blood, which formed the artisan class
and from which gradually emerged the middle class; and
the vast mass of the remaining population, of pure or
nearly pure Indian blood, which tilled the soil and per-
formed the menial tasks of society. There were, and are,
exceptions to the pattern, such as Argentina, Chile and
Uruguay, where the population is predominately European.

To take another consequence of the early social and
economic pattern, the Spanish crown granted huge tracts
of land to its sons who conquered the New World. Possession of the land meant virtual ownership of the people
living on it. The enormous supply of free labor dictated
the development of a plantation aristocracy startlingly similar to that of the ante-bellum South in the United States.
The labor surplus impeded industrial development, and
the feudal social pattern exerted a strong effect on the
direction of cultural development. Like the "well-bred"
Southern aristocrats, the Latin-American elite used its lei-
sure in the pursuit of culture. Wealthy landowners sent
their children to be educated in the best European schools,
or imported educated priests, nuns and professors from

Europe to take charge of schooling. Classical European culture became a status symbol.

In the northern United States, by way of contrast, labor was scarce because the western lands were free. Indentured servants and impoverished immigrants removed themselves from the labor pool at the first opportunity and swarmed to the frontier. Eastern capitalists were forced to develop labor-saving machinery—an impetus which was to stamp the United States as a nation of tinkerers, gadgeteers and, eventually, as creators of the assembly-line production system to supply the needs of a continent-wide market. In the bustling United States thrift and hard work were identified with religious virtue; wealth became a measure of value. There was little time for cultural refinements; they were left to the Boston "Brahmins"—a revealing appellation—and to the preachers and womenfolk.

There are many other obvious points of difference between Hispanic America and the United States. Obviously, the Roman Catholic church has left a deep and enduring mark on the area. What is less frequently recognized, however, is the extent to which the anti-clerical reaction, starting nearly one hundred years ago, is a key factor in the Hispanic-American social and political scene. The clash between clerical and anti-clerical factions today splits families, keeps political parties at each other's throats, exerts massive influence on governmental policy and is felt by many people to be at least as important as the outcome of the Cold War.

As still another example, the frontier in the United States has disappeared into legend, and its heroes and villains have been magnified by popular literature, motion pictures and television into greater-than-life size. In Latin America, on the other hand, almost every country has a still-unconquered frontier with all its attendant dirt, wretchedness, lawlessness and cheapness of life. This aspect shocks many a tourist accustomed to life in suburbia. It arouses a hypersensitive, chip-on-the-shoulder nationalism in many Latin Americans, who are reluctant to accept the fact that their countries have lagged behind Europe and North America in economic development. This inferiority complex is intensified by a condescending attitude or emotional rejection by North American tourists traveling through areas their grandfathers would have recognized immediately as "the wild and wooly West."

This hastily daubed backdrop serves only to establish a frame of reference for the North American reader who has never ventured south of the Rio Grande. It cannot take on meaning until a human being is set before it as a lens to bring it into emotional focus. That single figure raises the question: What do all the complex historical and environmental factors mean to the individual? How do they affect his responses to the daily round of life, love, suffering and death in which he is a participant?

One of the most rewarding ways of studying any culture is to become acquainted with its creative arts. Civilization and its techniques can be implanted in standardized form almost anywhere, and the twentieth century is filled with examples of peoples who have demanded the amenities of civilization without fully realizing that the process inevitably imposes upon them a standardization of personality as well. The factory system, apartment or slum life in a big city, anonymous education, mass entertainment and store-bought clothes, all contrive to smother individuality. Only the artist, occasionally, is able to recapture what is truest of his national temperament, heritage and environment.

The Latin-American scale of values sets creativity above cash. The social prestige accorded artistic expression is immense, and for many a talented young person of humble origin it is the only possible means of hurdling the rigid caste barriers that still exist in many of the countries. Far from apologizing for poetically inclined offspring, parents encourage youngsters to recite their poems at small social gatherings. Doctors, lawyers, politicians, social critics —historically, men (and women) of letters in Hispanic America have also been men of action, *hommes engagés*— often appear to take more satisfaction from the publication of a volume of verse or short stories early in their careers than from the years of professional achievement that followed. "Good morning, poet," is said to be a favorite salutation in some parts of Hispanic America (a more cautious variant being: "If you read yours, I'll read mine"), and, indeed, its use would seem to be amply justified.

However great the status value of a literary career may be to the writer, its material benefits are almost nonexistent. Unlike his North American counterpart, the Latin American cannot hope to earn a living by creative writing. There are few mass-circulation magazines comparable to those in the United States. Commercial periodicals and newspapers generally pay their contributors a token sum, or nothing. The writer, then, writes for the love of it or for the prestige value, but he lacks the disciplining spur of economic incentive.

A writer's creative efforts generally entail an out-of-pocket expense, for nearly all publishing houses demand that the author pay publication costs of his book—a system that exists in the United States only in the peripheral "vanity press." Even those who have achieved literary success, writers of the stature of Mexico's Alfonso Reyes, are frequently bound to this pernicious system. This means that the author faces a barrier of economic competence rather than of artistic merit. The average publishing house tends to treat his book as a job-printing order, and customarily loses interest in the edition as soon as the costs are paid and all copies are delivered into the author's hands.

Publicity and distribution are usually left to the author's initiative. As a consequence, a mediocre writer with a huckster's temperament often is better known and more widely read than a gifted writer who shrinks from vociferating his wares. Or, in self-defense, the young writer is forced to join a literary *capilla*, or clique, which disseminates the group's output by word-of-mouth advertising and biased literary reviews. Often a potentially great writer has sacrificed his talent to becoming the arbiter of his particular clique.

For these reasons, then, it is easier for contemporary European and United States authors to become known in any given Latin-American country than it is for authors living in the countries bordering it. Their literary output all too often is doomed by exigencies of economics and the market to becoming, in Vance Bourjaily's words, "the lost books of Latin America."

Hispanic America has a deep-rooted poetic tradition, the volume of poetry production greatly exceeding that of creative prose, be it the novel or short story. Rubén Darío, the great Nicaraguan lyric poet, took Europe by storm at the turn of the century as the apostle of "modernism," a movement born in Latin America. Some years later the Chilean poet, Vicente Hidobro, helped lay the foundations of the European surrealist movement with his "creationism." Hispanic-American poets, such as Pablo Neruda and Gabriela Mistral, the Nobel Prize winner, have since wielded increasing leverage in the international realm of letters.

Although the writing of poetry is a profoundly intimate experience, it is possible to detect pronounced stylistic trends in the work of the younger generation, and the strong, individual influences of such older Hispanic-American poets as César Vallejo, Nicolas Guillén, Pablo Neruda and Gabriela Mistral are apparent in many of the works included in this anthology. More surprising, perhaps, is the strong hold on the poetic imagination exercised by Walt Whitman, Edgar Allan Poe, T. S. Eliot, Ezra Pound, Stephen Spender and other North American and English models. The influence of the Spaniard Federico Garcia Lorca and of the German Rainer Maria Rilke is widespread, while the pull of the French moderns—André Breton, Luis Aragon and Paul Eluard—is also evident, though in lesser degree.

The approach to poetry charted by the Hispanic-American "vanguardist" and "realist" pioneers is still followed by large numbers of young writers. Surrealist influences linger in muted form here and there, while unabashedly lyrical poetry and purist-classical forms continue to win new recruits each year.

The realm of the short story, too, reveals an astonishing eclecticism among the younger writers, who are still flexing their literary muscles. A hypothetical average young Hispano-American writer might, in his first several books, skip blithely from a story of childhood in the Henry James tradition to a Kafkian nightmare about a government clerk to a regionalist tale of Steinbeckian cast to a stream-of-consciousness story bearing the Joyce imprint. It is expected that such young writers will continue to experiment until they enter the indefinable age of literary maturity and settle down to writing in a personal style about a preferred theme.

Humor appears to be a rare commodity among younger Hispano-American writers. They are, as a rule, deadly serious in their approach to letters, perhaps on the theory that "serious literature" must be serious. Much of their output falls into the "regional" category. Regionalism, or *criollismo* as it is called throughout a large part of Latin America, is an heir of the nineteenth-century Romantic movement. The American Romanticists were struck by the spectacle of man pitted against nature, or of man shaped by savage nature and pitted against his fellow man. The most frequent weakness of the genre is that its devotees are often so preoccupied with picturesque setting, dialect and other housekeeping details that the human beings in the stories come through only as puppets or stereotypes. Among the stories included in this volume, Juan Rulfo's "Talpa" and Porfirio Meneses' "The Little Dark Man" fall into the regionalist category, although each one is something more as well. "Like God," Antonio Marquez Salas' tale of Venezuelan *campesinos*, can also—by dint of a little shoehorning—fit into this wide category. In the hands of these sensitive and discerning artists, the *criollismo* becomes a universal human document.

From the regionalist theme of "man against nature," it is but a short step to the metropolitan writers whose theme is "man against the city." This growing group turns its back on the gaucho, the peasant and the timeless landscape. In many places—Uruguay comes to mind as a specific example—this revolt against what some consider to be an established literary vein is conscious, and self-styled "metropolitan" writers have banded together in an avantgarde. In other cases the choice seems to be haphazard; writers simply are exercising the storyteller's age-old privilege of working with the materials closest to hand. Writers of this bent are conscious of their national past, preoccupied with the passing of an old, aristocratic order and the rise of a new middle class of government clerks, shopkeepers and professionals. They depict characters whose lives more often than not are hard, tragic and bitter, but not hopeless, lives filled with vitality and a sense of individual worth. Some of the most acute insights into Hispanic America's tensions, its peculiar psychological and social problems, are to be encountered in this field. Mario Benedetti's "Gloria's Saturday," Julio Cortazar's "The Gates of Heaven," and Sebastián Salazar Bondy's "I'm Sentimental" are sample offerings by the city writers of the young generation.

Not surprisingly, a third major category is composed of stories which treat of "man against the system." In many Hispanic-American countries social contrasts offer a glaring target for indignation and protest. There are exploited classes, entire sections of the populace barred from education and other opportunities for self-advancement and doomed to misery and malnutrition. The young writer who uses his pen as a weapon of social protest is following a well-established tradition. Too often, however, indignation is an insufficient base for creativity. Too many authors fall into the easy posture of hurling ready-made cliches of "socialist realism" at the abstract target of injustice, and the magical transmutation of experience into art does not take place. In this anthology, Augusto Roa Bastos' "The Excavation" and Augusto Monterroso's "First Lady" are offerings by young writers who handle this demanding genre with more than ordinary skill.

The psychological story is also a widely diffused phenomenon among members of the young literary generation. René Marqués' portrait of the controversial Puerto Rican nationalist leader, Pedro Albizu Campos, and other stories in this collection reflect modern man's preoccupation with his inner world.

It is clear that, although occasional unity of purpose or style among young writers is evident in certain countries, the aforementioned groupings have no correlation to geographic boundaries. In general, a young writer is more apt to find kindred spirits separated from him by thousands of miles and a dozen national boundaries than existing in his own locality.

BLANCA VARELA

Lima, Peru, was Blanca Varela's birthplace (in 1926), but she has lived in Paris for several years. Her poems have appeared in a number of Mexican and Peruvian newspapers, magazines and anthologies.

Port Supe

My infancy is in this coast,
beneath the sky, towering
sky like no other, sky, swift shadow,
threatening clouds, dark whirlwind of wings,
blue houses on the horizon.
Next to the huge, windowless mansion,
next to the blind cows,
next to the turbid liquor and the carnivorous bird.
Oh, everyday sea,
mountain sea, rainy mouth of the cold coast!
There I destroy with an enormous rock
my father's house,
there I destroy the cage of the small birds,
I uncork the bottles and a black smoke escapes
and tenderly stains the air and the gardens.
There are my hours next to the dry river,
amid the dust and its palpitating leaves,
in the ardent eyes of this earth
where the sea throws its white dart.
One single season, one and the same time
of streaming fingers and odor of fish.
All one long night in the sand.

I love the coast, that dead mirror
where the air revolves insanely,
the wave of fire that demolishes corridors,
circus of shade and perfect crystal.

1

Here in the coast I climb a black well,
I come from the night toward the deep night;
I go beneath the wind that runs blindly,
my pupils luminous and empty.
Or I inhabit the interior of a dead fruit,
that suffocating silk, that heavy space
occupied by water and pale larvae.

In this coast it is I who awaken
among the foliage of brown wings,
I who occupy that empty branch,
I who do not want to see the night.

Here in the coast I have roots,
imperfect hands,
a burning couch where I weep alone.

Puerto Supe

Está mi infancia en esta costa,
bajo el cielo tan alto,
cielo como ninguno, cielo, sombra veloz,
nubes de espanto, oscuro torbellino de alas,
azules casas en el horizonte.
Junto a la gran morada sin ventanas,
junto a las vacas ciegas,
junto al turbio licor y al pájaro carnívoro.
¡Oh, mar de todos los días,
mar montaña, boca lluviosa de la costa fría!
Allí destruyo con una enorme piedra
la casa de mi padre,
allí destruyo la jaula de las aves pequeñas,
destapo las botellas y un humo negro escapa
y tiñe tiernamente el aire y los jardines.
Están mis horas junto al río seco,
entre el polvo y sus hojas palpitantes,
en los ojos ardientes de esta tierra
a donde lanza el mar su blanco dardo.

Una sóla estación, un mismo tiempo
de chorreantes dedos y aliento de pescado.
Toda una larga noche entre la arena.

Amo la costa, ese espejo muerto
en donde el aire gira como loco,
esa ola de fuego que arrasa corredores
circo de sombra y cristal perfecto.

Aquí en la costa escalo un negro pozo,
voy de la noche hacia la noche honda,
voy bajo el viento que recorre ciego
pupilas luminosas y vacías.
O habito el interior de un fruto muerto,
esa asfixiante seda, ese pesado espacio
poblado de agua y de pálidas larvas.

En esta costa soy el que despierta
entre el follaje de alas pardas,
el que ocupa esa rama vacía,
el que no quiere ver la noche.

Aquí en la costa tengo raíces,
manos imperfectas,
un lecho ardiente en donde lloro a solas.

Hugo Salazar Tamariz

The author of "The Roots" was born in 1923 in Cuenca, often called "the Athens of Ecuador." He is president of Horizonte, a national movement of Ecuadorian writers and artists, and the author of three volumes of poetry, a play and a novel.

The Roots

We are an ancient people,
                                  as old as honey,
as shadow,
                    as the high leaves,
so united to the rough bark that, from a distance,
no one would call us beings, but rather topography.
Stitched to the earth, we have been blue centuries
and bitter centuries, trampling the already interred
age of the mountain,
                                  the successive courses of the rivers
and eating the azymous concept of fruits.
Of jaguars,
                    of sun
                                  and stone hatchets,
we have gone on living
                                  and dying.
Strewn between wars
                                  and women we advance our murmuring
and the unaltered blood that buffets us.
We are an ancient people,
                                  resembling equally the light
or the shadows:
                    a flank in the snow
and green hung out to dry in mid-wind.
We have been growing without knowing it,

4

like flight in birds,
          like corn,
                  or the child,
like hair
       and fingernails;
                accumulating ourselves
like an electric charge
          or the interest on a debt.
How much hunger we have traversed on bare feet,
trampling on our stomachs
               amid the thronging people
who move continuously onward . . .

Hunger we could not quench even by elevating it
upon the backbone of our land;
hunger that we never digested,
                  dying
in beasts at nightfall,
          and in us enduring.
Hunger in the forests,
where we engendered our children against the ground,
                    and death,
with arrows
       and stones,
             in the wind.
We have been growing slowly,
             like fruit
or flavor in the seed,
          like virile odor of tree
or sound in the nocturnal wind that unites the terminal
sand and the hidden yearning.

An ancient people, alive as an ulcer,
alive as a flame.
We have had to journey far,
             sometimes from up to down,
like a tempest of rain,
         and other times,
              like lightning,

serpents
        or shadows.
An old people sketched in perfume,
                              with breasts
and thighs unclad,
                    convulsed in its mercurial destiny,
proclaiming a volcano at each step.
Even after death we have embraced the earth,
a thousand and thousand times,
                              as the most beloved woman;
it has been ours since condors were invented
and the sun imagined night.
We are an old people,
                  the earth is ours,
we love it,
        and stretch to embrace it,
                              face downwards,
with all our hunger
                and our children.
We have been,
                and we continue, inside the clod
that plows renew,
                and in the high fruit.
An old people not grown old, we have a multitude of light
and of grass,
            growing;
                  of doors
                        and windows,
                                    opened.
We have been coming until we number three million,
a gigantic wheat stalk,
                  an immense hand,
                              a net,
a branch,
        an entire people!
We are,
        with a vengeance,
                    a shout.

An old people, definitively green
                              and murmurous.
A people with three million windows
determined to open themselves.
No one seeing us,
                    from a distance,
                                        would think us to be,
without chance
                    or sunset,
                              but an audacious topography.

Las raices

Somos un pueblo antiguo,
                              viejo como la miel,
como la sombra,
                    como las altas hojas,
tan pegado a la áspera corteza que,
                                        de lejos
nadie nos diría seres sino topografía.
Zurcidos a la tierra hemos estado siglos azules
y amargos siglos,
                    hollando la ya enterrada
edad de la montaña,
                    los sucesivos cauces de los ríos
y comiendo del ácimo concepto de los frutos.
De jaguares,
          de sol
                    y hachas de piedra,
hemos ido viviendo
                    y falleciendo.
Regados entre guerras
                    y mujeres adelantamos nuestro rumor
y la intacta sangre que nos golpea entera.
Somos un pueblo antiguo,
                    parecido igualmente a la luz

o a las tinieblas:
                    un costado en la nieve
y el verde puesto a secar en la mitad del viento.
Hemos estado creciendo sin saberlo,
como el vuelo en las aves,
                    como el maíz
                              o el niño,
tal el pelo
        y las uñas;
                    acumulándonos,
como una carga eléctrica
                    o el interés en las deudas.
Cuánta hambre hemos atravesado a pie,
                              descalzos,
pisándonos el estómago,
                    entre la gente que va en tropel
que siempre estará yendo . . .

Hambre que no pudimos apagar ni elevándola
en la espina dorsal de nuestra tierra;
hambre que nunca digerimos,
                    muriendo,
en las bestias a la anochecida
                    y en nosotros durando.
Hambre en los bosques,
donde hicimos los hijos contra el suelo,
                              y la muerte,
con flechas
        y piedras,
              en el viento.
Hemos estado creciendo lentamente,
                    como el fruto
o el sabor en la semilla;
                    como viril olor de árbol
o sonido en el viento nocturno que une la arena del límite
y el soterrado anhelo.

Un antiguo pueblo vivo como una llaga
y vivo también como las llamas.

Ha tenido que andar mucho,
                    a veces de arriba abajo,
como la tempestad de lluvia,
                    y otras,
                              como el relámpago,
las serpientes
          o las sombras.
Un viejo pueblo pintado en el perfume,
                              con el pecho
y los muslos al aire,
                    convulso en su destino de mercurio,
proclamando un volcán a cada paso.
Hasta ya muertos nos hemos estado metiendo en la tierra,
mil
      y mil veces,
                    como en la más amada hembra;
la tenemos desde que se inventaron los cóndores
y el sol imaginó la noche.
Somos un pueblo viejo,
                    es nuestra la tierra,
la queremos
          y nos ponemos a abrazarla,
                              de bruces,
con toda nuestra hambre
                    y nuestros hijos.
Hemos estado,
          y seguimos, dentro del terrón
que mueven los arados
                    y en el alto fruto.
Viejo pueblo no envejecido porque tiene millones de luz
y de hierba,
          creciendo;
                    de puertas
                              y ventanas
                                        abiertas.
Hemos estado viniendo hasta ser tres millones,
una espiga gigante,
                una inmensa mano,
                              una red,

un ramal,
       un pueblo entero.
Somos,
      terriblemente,
           un grito.
Un viejo pueblo definitivamente verde
                 y rumoroso.
Un pueblo con tres millones de ventanas,
en voluntad de abrirse.
Nadie que nos viera,
           de lejos
               nos creyera,
sin acaso
      ni ocaso,
           sino una audaz topografía.

PORFIRIO MENESES

A writer and teacher, Meneses has published three collections of short stories, among them *El hombrecillo oscuro y otros cuentos*, from which the following story is taken. Born in Huanta, Ayaucho, Peru, in 1915, he has chosen to write about the Indian and mestizo types with which he is familiar.

The Little Dark Man

Northward from that corner you can see the old road to Lima losing itself in the distance. Behind us opens the pleasant, flowering serenity of the village's main plaza and we can hear a distant murmuring of tranquil people. To the left there is still another side street that little by little turns into a lane bordered by fences, submerged in the fragrance of the small ranches of Sancaypata.

It is a corner made for the sighs of those who see their loved ones leaving or who receive from time to time the surprise of novelties that the coast sends. In the afternoons the road's burden is always the same: the flock of sheep returning from pasture with its shepherd and its dogs, or the man with the burros who provides firewood for the village.

On that noon, near the corner, a gang of boys was laughing until the very roofs echoed. Suddenly there was a characteristic clattering. The sound might have been mistaken for that made by a string of horses drawing near, and in fact did soon resolve itself into the hoofbeats of an approaching cavalcade. The boys, naturally, left their games and ran to see the travelers whose arrival had been announced in this fashion. They formed a cortege of laughing glances, furtively running noses and small bare feet.

The man was serious—hermetic, you might say—and had very dark skin, which increased the bystanders' surprise and curiosity. Village bonhomie decreed that it was neces-

11

sary to follow the strangers at least with a smile. A lady in a kerchief interrupted her ancient tale of spurned love, told for the thousandth time to the same person, to say, "Oh, look!"

So her interlocutor could ask, as always in such cases: "Who could they be?"

Questions like this are common in the hill towns, and although they are always formulated, they generally remain unanswered. Or it may happen that the answer comes, but from the mouths of other people.

He was very dark; she, in contrast, was a flower. Even her horse was white, while his was a burnt sorrel. The third person in the group was a mule driver. His sweat-streaked face, a wad of coca and the mule ahead of him gave him away.

Instead of passing by as other travelers of previous days had done, the group turned left into the plaza. The man was impassive, looking for a store. By the time he was opposite one, the gang of boys was already large and all were staring boldly.

He dismounted.

Now many doors stood ajar, disclosing curious faces. You might say that the people already knew something but wanted to learn more. They turned to hypotheses and deductions, like the old men who win scientific contests.

The apricot tree was an old friend of mine. I frequently rested in its branches tasting the acid fruit. So when the mule driver came up to tie the mule's halter to my favorite tree, I thought it my right to ask: "Is he wild?"

But, no chance! This was one of many customary questions in the village. I would have preferred that he tie the mule at the foot of the *molle* tree, which was wormy and smelled bad. But I was very small then. And when one is small he doesn't argue with other people's decisions. This is only proper.

As I said, the dark man dismounted with a jingle of his small spurs. He approached the lady and, taking her by the waist, helped her down. Disgust wrinkled many eyebrows; our fellow man wants everything to be to his liking.

But it is better that things aren't that way, so the world is not one single color or one single measure.

She was beautiful and—wonder of wonders—had her hair caught up so that one could see a white, delicate neck, like none in my village, to say the least. Seeing the short, rather ugly man, some neighbors commented, "He must be a scribe."

"No, I'll bet he's a faith healer."

The majority accepted this idea. In truth, the stranger must have been very strange, since these kind people could not know that in the big cities the scribe's role is played by the lawyer and the faith healer's, I think, by the doctor. Distance permits such differences.

At any rate, we in Luracocha were indignant, at least the most important people were. How is it possible, we said—I, after the others—that a half-breed so small and so ugly can act like a husband toward such a beautiful girl? Of all the people I knew in the village, the one who seemed to be most ugly and unacceptable was the priest. The half-breed part didn't matter, although it really did. My neighbor, Don Manuel Quisoruco, for example, had a little Indian blood, but he had money. In contrast, the third senior justice of the peace was very white, even though he was always very dizzy from the amount of wine he drank. Many whites like him were drunker than the Indians of Chamana on a holiday. An aunt of mine often told me with a touch of pride:

"We come of a good family. Don't you see how everybody treats us considerately? There are Spaniards among our very recent ancestors. But I just don't understand how your mother married your father, who . . ."

As I have said, everybody in town was indignant. For that reason, the little groups that formed began to string together all sorts of conjectures. Somebody said that this trip was the epilogue of a bloody story: who knows in what village—but way beyond Jauja—there was a community of Indians whose chief was the dark man; there had been a fight over a question of land; all the landowners were killed, except the girl, who had been abducted (for a long time

that word rang in my ears until I came to learn that it
didn't mean much) by this man; and, in order to save her
honor, she had to follow him when he fled, before the
authorities from the capital arrived.

The bystanders became inflamed on hearing this story
and someone proposed that they seize the stranger and
give him an exemplary punishment, but our school teacher
cleared his throat, jingled the gold chain on his vest, and
said, louder than the rest:

"No, no, gentlemen. That's not how it was. What I
know is different, and there's no reason for me to keep still
or to lie. The thing happened . . ."

Then he told us a story of gratitude. The girl, who was
from the city of Huancavelica, had suddenly fallen ill with
a fever. Neither magic nor the herbs of all the healers of
the region had taken away her sickness. Somebody had
called the doctor; but, of course, the inevitable had occurred:
in addition to the fever, the girl began to suffer from colics
and fainting spells. Then providence had caused the dark
man to appear on some sort of business and someone had
recommended him. On receiving the task, he had imposed
the condition that nobody molest him when he was with the
patient. No one knows what he gave her, but soon they
could see she was improving. When she was completely
cured, the man saddled his horse one morning and said,
"I'm leaving." The girl was ready to follow him, and there
was nothing the family could say.

The people in the group told more stories—this, that and
the other—but the one I was inclined to believe, naturally,
was my teacher's.

The youngsters were a little confused and no longer felt
like beating the stranger; but still, I noticed that something
was brewing.

The driver's mule seemed peaceful at the foot of my
apricot tree in the plaza; the lady was dusting her skirt
and stretching beside her horse, and the man was buying
things to eat in a nearby store. But I was poking my nose
into each of the groups gathered near the fountain, in the
plaza, in Dona Visitacion's store, in front of the parish house

and in a few other places. The group with the worst things
to say was the one made up of church ladies.

Nearly all the boys, my schoolmates, were very near the
visitors. They circled around them at a certain distance, or
sat on the ground in order to eat peaches and see better.

The man visited several other stores; he seemed to be
looking for something that was unknown in the village. All
this increased the interest he had aroused. Besides, he
walked curiously: he wore high boots with buckles and
riding breeches that showed him to be bowlegged. He had
a big hat and, doubled over his shoulders, a white poncho
that made the color of his face and hands seem even darker.
He entered Dona Visi's store, where the governor's wife and
other esteemed ladies were gathered with their spinning
equipment. As he entered, he greeted them.

"May you have a good afternoon."

The ladies looked at each other; some of them answered
the greeting, but others did not. Dona Visitacion said:

"Good afternoon, sir. What may I offer you?"

"I would like a yard and a half of pink Madapollam," he
answered.

"Ah, what will you think!" she replied. "My store has the
largest stock around here, but right now I don't have what
you ask for. Wouldn't it be better to take Castile cloth, or,
if you want real quality, silk pongee?"

"No, ma'am, I wanted Madapollam," he answered courteously, and left.

I stayed in the doorway for a few seconds, but ran away
when I heard the outburst that followed, the most con-
siderate comment being, "Who does he thinks he is? Demanding Madapollam . . ."

When I caught up with the man again he was talking
with the girl and the mule driver. It appeared that they had
finished buying food and were planning to eat later outside
of town in the shade of a tree. I wouldn't say she looked
very elegant—her clothing was wrinkled—but the long,
shining earrings that reached her shoulders were striking.
Her face was like dawn and her skin as soft as the petal
of a flower. Over her gathered hair she wore a pleasing little

straw hat that protected her cheeks from the sun but let one see they were rosy. A flowered and fringed silk shawl covered her shoulders and back. In short, her pale hands and large eyes made her—I am sure—what my mother would have called "a beautiful lady," just as (she said) all those in our family were. And this one well deserved it.

I said the older boys were still restless. But they were always that way. I played a lot, like my schoolmates, but always in the classroom or around the fountain in the plaza. The most we ever did was to go and steal fruit from the gardens. But the older boys were always going to and fro with their guitars and their horses; they like to serenade and flirt with girls, and some of them even smoked. On Sundays they aroused my envy with their long, tight pants, their high shoes, coats and cat's-whisker ties blossoming from stiff collars. I wanted to be grown up and dress as they did.

Seeing that the strangers were preparing to continue their travels, the older boys reached a decision. Before that, my Cousin Santi told me, they had been arguing about what they should do. Not one thought that the girl should continue with so ridiculous a man. They thought of calling on the governor, but he was away in the provincial capital; the lieutenant was nothing but a half-breed, so they didn't even consider him. Somebody suggested the justice of the peace, but at his house they were told he had a cold. Everyone understood that he was drunk.

At last Nicolas Ruiz, who was the most important and audacious, said to the eight or nine boys surrounding him: "All right, boys, that's it. We'll have to take justice into our own hands."

"Hoo-o-o-ray!" the others chorused.

Old lady Conce, passing by and seeing the group, asked: "Why are they cheering for little Nicky? He's a promising lad, mark my words. I say that he's going to be provincial representative some day."

The boys cheered a little more and then scattered hurriedly. Meanwhile, the caravan of strangers left the plaza in the direction of the main highway on the road to Huanta.

All the houses and shops along the way were filled with curious stares and voices asking, "What do you think of that?"

The man went ahead on his big sorrel horse. He was very jaunty with his hunting jacket and his big hat. After him came the girl, riding sidesaddle, her costume harmonizing nicely with her white mare. The mule driver was behind, adjusting the cinch now and then or else whistling tunelessly. They passed the last streets of the village, the little exit bridge and the last houses. As the caravan receded down the wide highway shaded by *molle* and *retama* trees, I remained thoughtful: How fine it would be to have a shotgun loaded with rock salt and let it go in the faces of all the people who stood there staring incredulously down the road!

My thoughts were interrupted by Luis, the son of Don Cosme Santos, who came clattering up the street on his horse. Soon the other boys who had been cheering Nicky showed up. All began to caper about, brandishing their quirts, making their horses rear, and going through all sorts of antics while they waited for the ones who were missing. The priest emerged from his office, rubbing his bald head with his biretta, to ask, "Where are those fools going?"

The whole thing bothered me, because the fools weren't watching where their horses were going, and we small boys had to be dodging all the time, jumping into ditches so they wouldn't trample on us. In spite of that, I drew near Nick's group and learned that they were going to follow the man and take the girl away.

"And afterwards," one queried, "where will we take the girl?"

"To your house."

"Not to my house. What would my folks say? Your house would be better."

"No, not mine. Fermin, we'll take the girl to your house."

"To mine? And who's going to feed her if there's nobody home? I'm eating at my Aunt Tere's until my folks get back from Huancayo."

Nick had been looking from one to the other. At last he

exclaimed, "Why is everybody afraid of a woman? I'll take her with me."

Everybody was used to Nick's audacity, but what he had just said really surprised them. They asked themselves, as I did, what he would tell his parents to explain the arrival of the girl; but then, without any more thought, they shouted nearly together, "Fine! Fine, Nicky! Boys, three cheers for Nick Ruiz!"

A new hubbub started. Nicolas, reaffirming his attitude of daring and answering the cheers, continued:

"And if there's trouble, I'll get married, boys!"

"Fine! He's going to get married! Hip! Hip! Hooray!"

With the problem resolved, the boys whipped their horses, circled the plaza twice in a troupe and headed off down what they thought was the road to rescue.

Some people took them for reasonable boys; but others, then and always, thought them ragamuffins. I didn't know which party to join, but I found a burro with a straw mat saddle and along I went after the expedition.

They disappeared rapidly, leaving me only the dust of the road. However, I wasn't the only one pushed into the adventure by curiosity. Along with me came a band of small boys on foot, who bothered me by hanging on to the flanks of the burro. He kicked more than one of them soundly, a job in which I encouraged him with pleasure.

Preoccupied with the hard trot of my steed and the tugging of the boys, I didn't notice how close I was until the animal stopped short and I had to slide back from his ears. Before me was a sight that I thought heroic: the young riders were halted; beyond, facing them, were the strangers and, to their rear a small fordable river cut across the road.

When they caught up with the strangers, Nick had ordered, "Hey! Stop! Where are you taking that lady?"

"What do you mean, where?" the dark man had answered. "And who are you to be asking?"

Nick, wrathful, spoke in his turn with a dignified tone.

"I'm an honest man and not a vagabond! My friends and I have come to do justice."

"Very good!" the others had chorused, without understanding the "vagabond" part.

At that moment I arrived.

The riders were deliberating; they bunched their horses together, said something almost audible and then separated. I saw Jose Rojas, Pepecha, cupping his ears and shaking his head afterward as if he hadn't understood anything. The others did the same.

The man had turned his horse completely around and was gripping the whip end of his reins tightly, ready to repel any attack. The girl had placed herself behind him and was holding one of his arms, visibly frightened. The fool of a driver was cracking his whip to one side of the road, provoking a rush of anger in me.

"Let that lady go! You are taking her against her will."

"That's right, let her go," my Cousin Santi affirmed. "You have no right forcing her to follow you."

The man arched his eyebrows, turned towards the girl who was huddled like a kitten, and asked:

"Who am I taking against her will? Why don't I have a right? You don't know what you are talking about. This lady is my wife. But why do I have to explain anything to anybody. Martin! Let's go! Push our baggage through."

"No, no, my friend!" Nick interrupted. "Don't think it's going to be that easy. That lady is not willing nor is she your wife. You can't prove it."

"Ha, ha, ha!" the man burst out. "You make me laugh. Do I have to prove that she is my wife? Why not? Elisita, tell these boys that you are mine."

The girl, surprised, looked at the man, then at the boys and, covering her face, began to sob.

"Ah!" said one of the boys. "You see? She doesn't want to be with him. She isn't his wife."

"Of course she is! Elisita, darling, tell them you are my wife."

The little dark man had grown restless with the girl's tears and seemed to be unsure of her obedience. Women spoil everything when they cry. His voice took on a tone of supplication.

She uncovered her face and she was more beautiful than ever. I repeat, and will always maintain, that my mother would have been able to say this girl was of our family because of her beauty and her air of distinction. But my mother wasn't there, unfortunately. I can only imagine her words.

The half-breed kept on cracking his whip against the rocks, so enraging Jose Rojas that he ordered him to be quiet.

The half-breed looked at him insolently, and after an instant decided to keep on. Jose raised the end of his reins to slash at the driver, when the dark man shouted, "Quiet, Martin! Drive the mule on."

The other boys had been surrounding the group bit by bit. The man no longer felt sure of himself.

His nervousness was increased by the girl's apparent reluctance to clarify the situation. He looked at her fixedly, almost with anguish. She was resting on a lofty, distant pedestal of pride; but her glance was full of sweetness. It was not very audible, but I would swear that, finally, she opened her lips a little and said:

"He is my husband."

We smaller boys, somewhat farther away, were crestfallen to think that all that talk was going to end. I imagined the imminent fight: our boys with their quirts like the mule driver, and the man perhaps with a weapon that he carried, hidden. The idea alarmed me, but I didn't think of the prudent thing to do, which would have been to run away.

Nick, dignified and arrogant, approached the girl. I saw then that they indeed would make a good couple. He was really handsome. But that was only natural: in Luracocha, aside from those who have goiters, we are very presentable people.

"Tell me, Miss ——, or Mrs. ——," asked Nick, "are you really willing to go with this man?"

I think that all the birds and mosquitoes grew quiet so we could hear the reply. My heartbeat was the only sound. The man had backed away; I don't know whether he was getting ready to fight or whether he thought his cause was lost. Perhaps there was a threat in the obscure depths of his flinty eyes. In mid-river, while the mule drank, the half-breed resembled another figure of stone, only harder and darker.

The girl's face opened, after a long, long time, into a wide smile, white, pure. And then she said, "I am very grateful, gentlemen, but undoubtedly there is a misunderstanding here. The gentleman is my husband, and I go with him happily."

"Really?" Some of them marveled.

"Yes," she reaffirmed with a honeyed smile, and, turning her horse slowly, she set off.

Nick, his large, clear eyes filled with her, remained. So did we. On the other side of the river, the roadside trees hid the caravan. The boys burst out in noisy confusion until Nick grew angry.

"That's enough, boys! That's the way women are; they don't know what they want."

And we set off back down the road.

CARLOS CASTRO SAAVEDRA

Medellin, Colombia, was the birthplace of Carlos Castro Saavedra in 1924. Author of seven published volumes of poetry, his travels have taken him to Chile and to Europe. Nostalgic "home thoughts from abroad" echo from the lines of the following poem.

Wife America

I think of you from Europe, my wife,
I think of you in great strides, like a mad person,
and follow through all the countries and maps
your mountainous breast, your herds of milk,
and the desperate land of your volcanoes
and the scarred bark of your womb.

Between us the sea with its ships,
and the fields are between with their horses,
but the water cannot separate us;
neither the water nor the earth succeeds,
because I am the son you hold in your arms,
and you are the flame I have in my soul.

With kisses and with lips I exhume your forehead
of pure verdant resplendence,
hungrily I gnaw at hotels and countries,
gnaw at houses, villages, cemeteries;
and the towns taste of your face,
and the streets taste of your body.

The odor of your youthful land strikes me,
your savage perfume penetrates me,
and perfumes so much and so deeply,
that my skin smells of your green clothing,
and my poems smell of your life,
and my misfortunes smell of your death.

With clay of my clay, with loam of America,
with fire of your hands and my breath
you are making an American son;
I hear your labor from Europe,
I hear the growth of your clothing.

I keep vigil in Berlin, in Prague I keep vigil,
I feel your blood running under my bridges,
I feel that your harvests are spreading
along the hard walls, along my bed,
and that all the leaves of America and the rivers
and the revolutions burst in your breast.

Grow, wife, until I return,
my wife, wife of the mountains,
mother of the plowed lands and the winds;
Inez, your heart is like a fence
and I am a turbulent peasant
who sows you, I sow you about the world
and about the world I love you and remember you.

Esposa América

Te pienso desde Europa, esposa mía,
te pienso a grandes pasos, como loco,
y persigo por todas las patrias y los mapas
tu pecho montañoso, tus rebaños de leche,
y la desesperada tierra de tus volcanes
y la cicatrizada corteza de tu vientre.

Entre nosotros dos está el mar con sus barcos
y los campos están con sus caballos,
pero no alcanza el agua ni la tierra alcanza,
porque yo soy el hijo que tienes en los brazos
y tú eres el incendio que yo tengo en el alma.

Con besos y con labios desentierro tu frente
de puros resplandores vegetales,
hambrientamente muerdo hoteles y países,

muerdo casas, aldeas, cementerios,
y los pueblos me saben a tu cara
y las calles me saben a tu cuerpo.

Tu olor de tierra joven me golpea,
tu perfume salvaje me penetra
y me perfuma tanto y tan adentro,
que mi piel huele a tu vestido verde
y huelen mis poemas a tu vida
y mis desgracias huelen a tu muerte.

Con barro de mi barro, con arcilla de América,
con fuego de tus manos y mi aliento
estás haciendo un hijo americano;
yo escucho tu trabajo desde Europa,
escucho el crecimiento de tu vientre
y escucho el crecimiento de tu ropa.

Me desvelo en Berlín, en Praga me desvelo,
siento correr tu sangre por mis puentes,
siento que tus cosechas se propagan
por las paredes duras, por mi lecho,
y que todas las hojas de América y los rios
y las revoluciones estallan en tu pecho.

Sigue creciendo, esposa, mientras vuelvo,
esposa mia, esposa de los montes,
madre de los arados y los vientos;
Inés, tu corazón es como un surco
y yo soy un labriego turbulento
que te siembro, te siembro por el mundo
y por el mundo te amo y te recuerdo.

Ernesto Cardenal

Born in Granada, Nicaragua, in 1925, Cardenal studied at the universities of Mexico and Columbia (New York City). His work —which has appeared in newspapers, magazines and anthologies —has been influenced to a great extent by contemporary North American poetry. The poem that follows tells in flashbacks of American filibuster William Walker, who joined a revolutionary faction in Nicaragua, became president in 1856, and four years later met death at the hands of a firing squad in Honduras.

With Walker in Nicaragua

In a lonely cabin on the border,
I, Clinton Rollins, without literary pretension,
entertain myself by writing my memoirs.
    And my old man's thoughts turn backward:

The things that happened fifty years ago . . .
Hispano-Americans I have known
    —whom I have learned to love.
And that warm, sweet, green odor of Central America.
The white houses with red roofs and with wide, sun-
  splashed eaves,
and a tropical patio with a fountain and a woman by the
  fountain.
And the heat made our beards grow.
The scenes that come back to my memory now!
A gray wave that advances blotting out the hills
and a muffled hiss of cloudburst running through the jungle
and the howl of the monkeys on the opposite bank
and afterward the heavy, metallic battering of raindrops on
  the zinc roofs
and they run to take in the clothes from the ranch porches
and later the gray wave and the muffled hiss moving off
and once again the silence . . .

And how it smelled of underbrush and the river became
    colored with chlorophyll,
how the steam appeared fresh and tranquil
beneath the blue shade of the forest;
and the sudden dive of an iguana into the water,
the rumble of falling tree trunks,
the distant report of a rifle,
a word in Spanish shouted from afar,
the laughter of the Negro girls washing clothes
and a Caribbean song.

My companions on that expedition with William Walker:
Achilles Kewen, the aristocrat, who fell fighting in Rivas;
Chris Lily, the boxer,
his throat cut while drunk one night beside a shining lagoon;
William Stocker (Bill), with his pirate's face—a good man—
who married there afterward and lived beside the lake of
    Managua,
and I ate once in his house;
and Crocker, the effeminate,
who gasped out his life in Rivas,
with his dirty, blond beard heavy with blood,
with one arm dangling and in the other a half-empty
revolver;
Skelter, the petulant one, who died of cholera;
and Dixie, the newsboy—the bugler—
on the night Colonel Jack broke through the lines
was better than the Scottish bagpipes at Lucknow
playing his bugle.
De Brissot, Dolan, Henry, Bob Gray;
the bandit, the disillusioned, the tramp, the treasure-seeker;
the ones who stayed hanging from the trees and swinging
beneath the stinking black condors and the moon
or sprawled on the plains with one lone coyote and the
    moon,
a rifle beside them;
or in the hot, cobbled streets filled with shouts,
or white like seashells on the beach
where the tides are always covering and uncovering them.

Those who passed through all those dangers and are still
   alive.
Those who stayed on to marry there afterward
and to live in peace in that land
and who, this afternoon, may sit remembering,
(perhaps thinking of writing, some day, their memoirs . . .)
and their wife who is of that land, and the grandchildren
   playing.
Those who deserted with Turley, inland, toward the gold
   mines
and were surrounded by natives and perished.
The man who fell, sleeping, from a boat
—dreaming perhaps of battles—
and no one heard his cries in the darkness,
if he did cry.
Those who were shot by Walker against a gray church.
   And afterwards, Walker himself, shot . . .
Hornsby had been in Nicaragua
and he spoke of its blue lakes between blue mountains
   under a blue sky,
and that it was the transit route and the great way,
the wharf of America,
and that it would fill with merchant ships and with
   foreigners
speaking all languages, waiting for the Canal,
and each ship bringing new adventurers,
and the green plantations and their great, white houses with
   terraces,
and the planter's wife teaching the children of the Negroes,
and the fields with saw mills and avenues of palms and the
   sound of sugar mills
and the roads filled with blue coaches
and the canoes going down the rivers.

I saw Walker for the first time in San Francisco:
I remember him as if I were seeing his blond face like a
   tiger's;
his gray eyes, without pupils, unmoving like a blind man's,
but which dilated and lit up like gunpowder in combat,

his skin of blurred freckles, his paleness, his clergyman's
      manners,
his voice, colorless like his eyes, cold and edged,
in a lipless mouth.
And a woman's voice was no softer than his:
that of the serene announcement of death sentences . . .
That which dragged so many into the maw of death in
      combat.
He never drank or smoked and he wore no uniform.
Nobody was his friend.
And I don't remember ever having seen him smile.

Con Walker en Nicaragua

En una cabaña solitaria en la frontera,
yo, Clinton Rollins, sin pretención literaria,
me entretengo en escribir mis memorias.
                    Y mis pensamientos de viejo retroceden:

Las cosas que hace cincuenta años sucedieron . . .
Hispanoamericanos que he conocido
                    —a los que he aprendido a querer.
Y aquel olor tibio, dulzón, verde, de Centro América.
Las casas blancas con tejas rojas y con grandes aleros llenas
      de sol,
y un patio tropical con una fuente y una mujer junto a la
      fuente.
Y el calor hacía crecer nuestras barbas.
¡Las escenas que hoy vuelven a mi memoria!
Una ola gris que viene borrando los montes
y un sordo rumor de inundación recorriendo la selva
y los aullidos de los monos en la margen opuesta
y después las gotas de gruesos metálicos golpes en los techos
      de zinc
y corren a quitar la ropa en las barandas de las haciendas
y después la ola gris y el sordo rumor alejándose
y otra vez el silencio . . .

Y cómo olía a maleza y el río se coloreaba de clorofila,
cómo fresco y tranquilo el vapor se divisaba
bajo la sombra azul de la selva;
y el repentino planazo de la iguana en el agua,
el estruendo de los troncos cayendo,
el disparo distante de un rifle,
una palabra en español que gritan lejos,
la risa de las negras lavando la ropa
y un canta caribe.

Mis compañeros en aquella expedición con William Walker:
Aquiles Kewen, el aristócrata, que cayó peleando en Rivas;
Chris Lily, el boxeador,
degollado borracho una noche frente a una resplandeciente
        laguna;
William Stocker (Bill), con su cara de pirata—y buen
        muchacho—
que se casó allá después y vivía junto al lago de Managua,
y yo comí una vez en su casa;
y Crocker, el afeminado,
que murió jadeante en Rivas,
con su sucia barba rubia pesada de sangre,
con un brazo colgándole y en el otro a medio descargar
el revólver;
Skelter, el petulante, que murió del cólera;
y Dixie, vendedor de periódicos,—el corneta—
que mejor que las gaitas escocesas en Lucknow,
la noche que el coronel Jack rompió las líneas
tocó esa corneta.
De Brissot, Dolan, Henry, Bob Gray;
el bandido, el desilusionado, el vago, el buscador de tesoros;
los que quedaron colgados de los árboles y meciéndose
bajo los hediondos cóndores negros y la luna
o tendidos en los llanos con un coyote sólo y la luna,
el rifle junto a ellos;
o en las calientes calles empedradas llenas de gritos,
o blancos como conchas en la costa
donde las mareas los están siempre cubriendo y descu-
        briendo.

Los que pasaron todos esos peligros y viven todavía.
Los que se quedaron para casarse allá después
y vivir en paz en esa tierra
y estarán esta tarde sentados recordando,
(pensando escribir tal vez un día sus memorias . . .)
y su esposa que es de esa tierra, y los nietos jugando.
Los que desertaron con Turley, adentro, hacia las minas de
      oro
y fueron rodeados por nativos y perecieron.
El hombre que cayó dormido desde un barco
—soñando tal vez con batallas—
y nadie oyó sus gritos en la oscuridad
si es que gritó.
Los que fueron fusilados por Walker contra una iglesia gris.
              Y después, el propio Walker, fusilado . . .
Hornsby había estado en Nicaragua
y hablaba de sus lagos azules entre montes azules bajo el
      cielo azul,
y que era la ruta del Tránsito y la gran vía,
el muelle de América,
y que se llenaría de barcos mercantes y de extranjeros
hablando todas las lenguas, esperando el Canal,
y cada barco trayendo nuevos aventureros,
y las verdes plantaciones y sus grandes casas blancas con
      terrazas,
y la esposa del plantador instruyendo a los hijos de los
      negros,
y los campos con aserríos y avenidas de palmeras y rumores
      de ingenios
y los caminos llenos de diligencias azules
y las tucas bajando los ríos.

Ví por primera vez a Walker en San Francisco:
recuerdo como si lo viera su rostro rubio como el de un
      tigre;
sus ojos grises, sin pupilas, fijos como los de un ciego,
pero que se dilataban y se encendían como pólvora en los
      combates,

y su piel de pecas borrosas, su palidez, sus modales de
    clérigo,
su voz, descolorida como sus ojos, fría y afilada,
en una boca sin labios.
Y la voz de una mujer no era más suave que la suya:
la de los serenos anuncios de las sentencias de muerte . . .
La que arrastró a tantas a la boca de la muerte en los
    combates.
Nunca bebía ni fumaba y no llevaba uniforme.
Ninguno fué su amigo.
Y no recuerdo haberle visto jamás sonreír.

JUAN RULFO

The world of fact and fantasy, of realism and make-believe, meet and mingle in Rulfo's writings. Translation of his work into English, French, Italian, German, Czech and Swedish has given him an international audience, and his *El llano en llamas*, recognized as one of Mexico's contemporary classics, has gone into three editions. Born in Sayula, Jalisco, Mexico, in 1918, and winner of a Rockefeller Foundation scholarship, Juan Rulfo is acknowledged as one of the best of the younger Spanish-speaking short story writers.

Talpa

Natalia slipped into her mother's arms and for a long time cried softly. They were sobs held back for many days —until now, when we had returned to Zenzontla, and Natalia saw her mother and began to feel a need for comforting. But before—during the labors of so many hard days, when we had to bury Tanilo in a hole in the earth of Talpa without anyone to help us, when she and I, the two of us alone, joined our strength to dig the grave, burrowing in the ground with our hands, hurrying to hide Tanilo in the ground quickly so that never again would he frighten anybody with his odor and look of death—during that time she did not cry.

Nor did she cry afterwards, during our return, when we came walking by night, knowing no peace, groping our way like sleepwalkers, and moving with steps that seemed to beat on Tanilo's grave. Then Natalia seemed to be hardened and to have constricted her heart so as not to hear its noise inside her. But no tears came from her eyes.

She came all the way here to cry; clinging to her mother, just to grieve her and to let her know she was suffering; bothering all of us at the same time because I felt her crying inside myself, too, as if I were wringing out the rag of our sins.

Because the fact is that Natalia and I between us killed Tanilo Santos. We took him to Talpa so he would die. And he died. We knew he couldn't stand so much walking; but we took him anyway, pushing him on, the two of us, thinking to finish him for good. We did that.

The idea of going to Talpa was my brother Tanilo's. It occurred to him before anyone else. For years he had been asking us to take him; for years, since the day he awoke with purple blisters sprinkled over his arms and legs. Later the blisters turned into sores from which came no blood but a yellow resin-like substance. From that time on, I remember very well, he told us how afraid he was that there was no cure. Because of that he wanted to go and see the Virgin of Talpa, so that she would cure his sores with her eyes. Even though he knew that Talpa was far away and that we would have to walk a long way under the sun of the March days and in the cold of its nights—even so, he wanted to go. The Virgin would cure him of those sores that never dried. She knew how to do that: to wash things, to renew things, like a field after the rain. Once in front of her all his ills would end; nothing would hurt him or return to bother him again. That is what he thought.

And we used that, Natalia and I, to take him. I had to go with Tanilo because he was my brother. Natalia had to go along, too, at all costs, because she was his wife. She had to help him, holding his arms, supporting him with her shoulders, on the way to Talpa and maybe on the return, while he dragged his hope along.

I already knew what Natalia felt inside. I knew something about her; that she had been lonely for a long time. I already knew that. We had been together many times; but always the shadow of Tanilo kept us apart. We felt that his blistered hands came between us and carried Natalia away so that she would keep on nursing him; and we knew that it would always be like that as long as he lived.

I know that now Natalia is sorry for what happened.

And I am too; but this will not save us from remorse, nor will it let us have peace ever again. It can't help us to know that Tanilo would have died anyway, and that going to Talpa, so distant, so far away, didn't make any difference. Because it is almost certain that he would have died just the same here as there, or maybe a little bit later here than there. All that he suffered on the road, the extra blood he lost, and the courage—all of those things together were what killed him sooner. The bad thing is that Natalia and I pushed him on when he didn't want to go on any longer, when he felt it was useless to go on and begged us to go back. We would pull him up from the ground so he would keep on walking, telling him that we could no longer go back.

"It is closer to Talpa than to Zenzontla," we told him. But even then Talpa was still distant, still many days away.

What we wanted was for him to die. You could even say that was what we wanted before we left Zenzontla and during each of the nights that we spent on the road to Talpa. It is something we can't understand now; but it was what we wanted then. I remember very well.

I remember those nights very well. First, we made a fire of torchpine. Afterwards, we would let the ashes dim the fire and then Natalia and I would hunt for some shadow to hide ourselves from the light of the sky. So we became part of the loneliness of the country, away from Tanilo's eyes and disappearing in the night. And that loneliness pushed us together. . . .

It always happened that the earth on which we slept was warm. And the flesh of Natalia, the wife of my brother Tanilo, became warm immediately with the warmth of the earth. Those two warmths together would begin to burn and make me awaken from my sleep. Then my hands would go behind her. They would come and go over this something like a bed of coals which was Natalia, first gently but then gripping her as if wanting to squeeze the blood out of her, time and again, night after night, until dawn came and the cold wind put out the fire in our bodies. This,

Natalia and I did alongside the road to Talpa when we took Tanilo for the Virgin to heal him.

Now everything is over. Tanilo is healed even of living. He can no longer say anything about the hard work it cost him to live. But now that he is dead, everything looks different. Now Natalia cries for him, maybe so he can see, from wherever he is, all the great remorse that weighs on her soul. She says she has felt the face of Tanilo these last days. It was the only thing of his that meant anything to her. The face of Tanilo, always damp with the sweat of his efforts to bear his pain. She felt it drawing near her mouth, hiding itself in her hair, asking her, with a murmur, to help him. She says that he told her he was finally cured, that no pain bothered him any longer.

"Now I can be with you, Natalia. Help me to be with you," she says he told her.

We had just left Talpa, left Tanilo covered over in that sort of deep rut that we made to bury him in.

And Natalia forgot about me from then on. I know how her eyes shone before like two pools lighted by the moon. But suddenly they faded, their look was erased as if it had been trampled in the dirt. And she seemed not to see anything. All that existed for her was her Tanilo, whom she had nursed while he was alive and whom she had buried when he had to die.

It took us twenty days to reach the main highway to Talpa. All that time the three of us had been walking alone. But from Talpa onward we began to join people coming from everywhere, who had flowed like us into that wide highway, that river current dragging us along, pushing on all sides as if they were carrying us along bound together with fibers of dust. The swarms of people stirred up a dusty white corn chaff that rose man high and fell again. The dust was above and below us all the time. And above the earth the sky was empty, cloudless. There was only dust; but dust provides no shade. We had to wait for nightfall to rest from the sun and that white light of the highway.

Then the days began to lengthen. We had left Zenzontla

in the middle of February, and now that March was beginning dawn came early. We would barely close our eyes at darkness when the sun would wake us again, the same sun that had just set.

And I had never felt life to be so slow or brutal as when walking in a crowd of people, just as if we were a mass of worms balled together under the sun, squirming inside the cloud of dust that hemmed all of us into the same path and herded us along. Our eyes followed the dust cloud; they struck against the dust as if stumbling over something they could not penetrate. And the sky was always gray, like a gray, heavy stain that pressed down on all of us from above. Only at times, when we would cross a river, was the dust higher and clearer. We would duck our heated, dust-coated heads into the green water and for a moment, from all of us, a blue smoke would rise, like the vapor that leaves your mouth in the cold weather. But shortly afterward, we would disappear again, mingled together in the dust, sheltering each other from the sun, from the sun's heat distributed among us all.

Some day, we thought, night would arrive. Night would arrive and we would rest. Now it was a matter of crossing the day, of getting through it somehow, of fleeing from the heat and the sun. Afterward, we would stop . . . afterward. What we had to do now was to make effort after effort, to hurry along behind the many like ourselves and ahead of the many others. That was what mattered. We would rest for good when we were dead.

That is what Natalia and I thought of, and perhaps Tanilo did too, as we trudged along the main highway to Talpa amid the procession, wanting to be the first to reach the Virgin before the miracles gave out. But Tanilo began to grow worse. The time came when he didn't want to go on. The soles of his feet were cracked and blood was beginning to seep from the cracks. We took care of him until he was better, but even so he no longer wanted to go on.

"I'll stay here resting a day or two and then I'll go back to Zenzontla," he told us.

But Natalia and I didn't want him to go back. Something inside us kept us from feeling any pity for Tanilo. We wanted to reach Talpa with him because, the way he was now, he was still too much alive. So while Natalia rinsed his feet with *aguardiente* to reduce the swelling, she encouraged him. She told him that only the Virgin of Talpa could cure him. *She* was the only one who could bring him relief forever—*she,* no one else. There were many other Virgins, but only the one of Talpa was any good, Natalia told him.

Then Tanilo would start crying, the tears drawing lines down the dirt on his face, and he would curse himself for having acted badly. Natalia would wipe the stream of tears with her shawl, and she and I between us would lift him from the ground so he could walk for a while longer before night fell. In that way, pulling him along, we arrived at Talpa.

During those last days too we grew tired. Natalia and I felt our bodies sagging more and more. It was as if someone had loaded a heavy weight upon us to hold us back. Tanilo fell down more frequently, and we had to pick him up and sometimes carry him on our shoulders. Maybe because of that, we had become the way we were: our bodies limp and tired, sick of walking. But the people moving along near us made us walk faster.

At night the flow of people stopped. There were campfires scattered everywhere. Around the fires our fellow pilgrims said their beads, arms extended in the form of a cross, looking toward the sky of Talpa. And one could hear how the wind carried the murmur, intermingling it to make it a single groan. A little later everything grew quiet. About midnight we would hear someone singing far away. Then we would close our eyes and wait without sleeping for dawn to come.

We entered Talpa singing the Te Deum.

We had left Zenzontla the middle of February and arrived at Talpa during the last days of March, when many were already leaving. Tanilo began to do penance. When he saw himself surrounded by men who wore cactus leaves hanging like capes, he thought of wearing his. He took to tying his feet together with the sleeves of his shirt so that his steps were even more faltering. Later he wanted to wear a crown of thorns. Later still he blindfolded himself and then, on the last stretch of road, he knelt on the ground. In this fashion, shuffling on his knees with his hands crossed behind him, the thing that was my brother Tanilo Santos arrived at Talpa.

And when we least expected it, we saw him joining in the dances. We scarcely had time to realize it, and there he was with a long rattle in his hand, stamping on the ground with his bruised, bare feet. He seemed possessed by a fury, as if shaking off the anger that he had borne for such a long time, or as if making one last effort to continue living a while longer.

Perhaps when he saw the dances he had remembered how he used to go every year to Tolimán for the novena of the Lord, and how he used to dance all night long until his bones were weak, but without ever getting tired. Maybe he had remembered that and wanted to call back again his old strength. Natalia and I saw him like that for a moment.

Suddenly he raised his arms and flung his body to the ground, the rattle still shaking in his blood-spattered hands. We dragged him away, hoping to protect him from the kicking of the dancers, away from the fury of those feet that whistled over the stones, jumping and stamping the earth without knowing that something had fallen among them.

Carrying him between us, we went into the church. Natalia helped him kneel close to her, right in front of the little gilded figure that was the Virgin of Talpa. And Tanilo began to pray. A huge tear brimmed up over his eyelid and splashed down onto the candle that Natalia had placed in his hands, putting out the flame. But he did not notice; the glow of so many lighted candles there blinded him to what was happening. He went on praying with his dead candle, praying in shouts so that he could hear what he was praying.

"... *from our hearts there goes out to Her the same supplication, enveloped in sorrow, many lamentations min-*

gled with hope. *Her tenderness is not dulled by either laments or tears, because She suffers with us. She can erase that stain and make the heart tractable and pure to receive Her mercy and Her charity. Our Virgin, our mother, who wishes to know nothing of our sins, who assumes the guilt for our sins, who would like to bear us in Her arms that life might not injure us, is here close to us, alleviating our weariness and the illness of our souls and our crushed, wounded, beseeching bodies. She knows that each day our faith is greater because it is built of sacrifices. . . ."*

The priest spoke thus from high up in the pulpit. When he stopped talking, everybody burst out praying at the same time with a noise like a swarm of wasps frightened by smoke. But Tanilo had not heard the priest's words. He remained quiet, his head resting on his knees. And when Natalia touched him so that he would get up, he was already dead.

Outside we could hear the sound of the dances, the drums and the pipes, the ringing of the bells. That was when the sadness hit me. To see so many living things—to see the Virgin there, right in front of us, smiling at us, and to see Tanilo on the other side, as if he were a cast-off garment—made me sad. But we had brought him there so he would die, that is what I can't forget.

Now we two are back in Zenzontla. We have returned without him, and Natalia's mother has asked me nothing—not what I did with my brother Tanilo, nothing. Natalia has started to cry on her shoulder, and in that way has told her everything that happened.

And I am beginning to feel as though we haven't arrived anywhere; that we are here for a while, to rest, and that then we'll go on walking. I don't know where, but we must go on. We are even beginning to be afraid of each other. This business of not saying anything to one another since leaving Talpa—because here we are too close to remorse and to the memory of Tanilo. Maybe that's what it means.

Alfredo Cardona Pena

A native of Costa Rica, born in the capital city of San Jose in 1917, is this author of six volumes of verse. He teaches courses in Spanish literature at summer sessions of the University of Mexico, and, in 1951, he won the Inter-American Prize for poetry.

My Aunt Esther

My aunt Esther, sister of Agueda Velarde,
freshens my memory like a gentle rain,
and also—oh, St. Victor!—
like a Philidor sonata
played on an old, gilded claviehord.
She comes from re-melted bells,
from cherished furniture and shadows
to peck my brow in the night
like a harassed swallow.

My aunt Esther, ancient,
was solitude itself in company.

She was the rue and certain sad plants
of my childhood, and I still perceive
the biblical thyme of her name
and the silent moon of her steps.

She was domestic, as spoons are,
and in the family converse left
the flavor of wild marjoram, which
she gathered in silence. (For she had
a sad solemnity. I have already told you
she was the sister of Agueda Velarde.)
She rose with the bread and went
about her mystical tasks,
leaving in the streets the decorum

40

of an antique engraving.
(Her gowns smelled of withered cypress,
and the rustle of leaves fell from her skirts.)

Sleeping in her spinster's bracken
she organized the meeting of saints,
and then she visited the sick
with a basket of fruit,
for she had the knack of morning.

Tenuous phantom of mine, of my blood.
The wardrobes still keep her emblems
and her memory falls in my bell
like rain upon the quince trees.

Mi tía Esther

Mi tía Esther, hermana de Agueda Velarde,
llega hasta mi recuerdo como una lluvia fina,
y también—oh St. Victor—
como una sonata de Philidor
tocada sobre un viejo clavicordio dorado.
Viene de las campanas ya fundidas,
de los muebles amados y las sombras
a picotear mis sienes en la noche
como una golondrina perseguida.

Mi tía Esther, anciana,
era la soledad en compañía.

Era la ruda y ciertas matas tristes
de mi niñez, y aún percibo
el bíblico tomillo de su nombre
y la callada luna de sus pasos.

Era casera como las cucharas,
y en la tertulia familiar dejaba
el sabor del orégano, que luego
recogía en mutismos. (Pues tenía

solemnidad luctuosa. Ya os he dicho
que era hermana de Agueda Velarde.)
Se levantaba con el pan e iba
a sus faenas místicas,
dejando por las calles el decoro
de una lámina antigua.
(Olían sus cotonas a cipreses marchitos
y el rumor de las hojas caía de sus faldas.)

Dormida en sus helechos de soltera
organizaba el mítin de los santos,
y luego visitaba enfermedades
con un cesto de frutas
porque tenía el don de la mañana.

Fino fantasma mío, de mi sangre.
Los roperos aún guardan sus emblemas
y su recuerdo cae en mi campana
como la lluvia sobre los membrillos.

Alberto Ordonez Arguello

Born in 1914 in the town of Rivas, on the shores of Lake Nicaragua, this writer has published one volume of poetry, a play and a novel. Here he has taken his theme from an ancient Mayan poem—in the italicized stanzas—and has embroidered his own pattern upon it. The volcano of Izalco, referred to in the poem, has been active since 1777; its glow can be seen from the Pacific Ocean.

Song of Neztahualcoyotl

I

Mother of mine, when I die
bury me 'neath the hearth
and when you make the bread, pause
and weep a little for me.

Maiden of early dawn,
morning will spread its fragrance
between the earth and the sea,
mother of mine, when I die.

Not upon any earth,
but only where rises the song
of the turtle dove in spring,
there I wish to rest!
Mother of mine, when I die,
bury me 'neath the hearth.

An April completely aflame
will come to gild the cornfield;
mother of mine, when I die
light the fire in the hearth
and when you make the bread, pause.

Above its green pennant
the banana tree will raise

43

the red blossom which was I.
You must pluck that blossom,
mother of mine, when I die
and weep a little for me.

II

And if someone seeks to know
the reason for your sorrow,
tell him the wood is green
and the smoke makes you cry.

And if someone seeks to know
why the salt spray of the sea
leaves its bitterness on the rock.

And if someone seeks to know
under the wave-wasted night
the reason for your sorrow,
tell him, mother, as you sigh:
"The one my dreams now dream of
never, nevermore will dream."

And if someone seeks to know
—when among the rocks and the tangle
the river breaks into song—
the reason for your sorrow,
say an infinitesimal happiness
left in your breast as remembrance
the wound of the balsam tree.

And if someone seeks to know
why your golden-hued face
watches the passing clouds,
say that the cloud has taught you
—mother of mine, gentle mistress—
the reason for your sorrow.

And if someone seeks to know
whether the volcano moon

is the reason for your sorrow,
a breeze from the groves of Izalco
shall remind you of my love;
and as you sit before the hearth
tell him the wood is green
and the smoke makes you cry.

Canción de Neztahualcoyotl

Madre mía, cuando muera
sepúltame en el hogar
y al hacer el pan, espera
y por mí ponte a llorar.

Siguapil de luz primera,
la mañana ha de aromar
entre la tierra y el mar,
madre mía, cuando muera.

No sobre tierra cualquiera,
sí donde habrá de cantar
la tórtola en Primavera,
¡allí quiero descansar!
Madre mía, cuando muera,
sepúltame en el hogar.

Un abril de llama entera
vendrá el maizal a dorar;
madre mía, cuando muera
enciende el fuego del lar
y al hacer el pan, espera.

Sobre su verde bandera
levantará el platanar
la roja flor que yo era.
Habrás la flor de cortar
madre mía, cuando muera
y por mí ponte a llorar.

II

Y si uno en saber se empeña
la causa de tu penar,
dile que verde es la leña
y que el humo hace llorar.

Y si uno en saber se empeña
por qué la espuma del mar
deja su amargo en la peña.

Y si uno en saber se empeña
bajo la noche mareña
la causa de tu penar,
dile, madre, al suspirar:
"a quien ya mi sueño sueña,
nunca más ha de soñar."

Y si uno en saber se empeña
—cuando en la piedra y la breña
el río rompe a cantar—
la causa de tu penar,
di que una dicha pequeña
dejó en tu pecho por seña
la herida del balsamar.

Y si uno en saber se empeña
por qué tu cara trigueña
mira las nubes pasar,
di que la nube te enseña
—madre mía, dulce dueña—,
la causa de tu penar.

Y si uno en saber se empeña
si es la luna volcaneña
la causa de tu penar,
brisa de huerta izalqueña
mi amor te hará recordar;
y ante la lumbre hogareña,
dile que verde es la leña
y que el humo hace llorar.

ANTONIO MARQUEZ SALAS

The author of this intensely Faulknerian tale of Venezuelan *campesinos* was born in Merida, south of Lake Maracaibo, in 1919. Two volumes of his short stories have been published.

Like God!

Over the earth appeared a green hand and with its striated, innumerable fingers it began to weave a liquid carpet of smoke. In the beginning was the smoke, were eyes fleeing like birds and metallic sounds carried by the wind. It was mud that was deposited on the river, thick with pigs and drowned dogs. In the beginning was the field sown with corn, with its flowers of rabid plumage and its yellow beard floating unkempt like a cloud of drunken locusts.

Autilo contemplated the night being born with fixed eyes that widened in the measure that darkness touched the stars; meanwhile, beneath his feet, his foot, or better yet his fingers, or the only finger that left a mark, the sand filtered like invisible water, pale, fine and pale, as if it were lightly soaked with blood.

Seated alone in the patio, resting his body against the wall, he waited for someone to come and take for him the steps that were denied him; in the meantime he contented himself with breathing the strange perfume the air brought and with feeling beneath his legs the soft itching of the sand. From the depths of the countryside, as though through a horn, the voice of Lura Magina seemed to come to him. Light and shadow mingled like a disturbed crowd and the air was smudged with intense, muffled noises. Autilo crumbled the livid pulp of a stem between his fingers.

Lura Magina was midway between Lesubia and his life. Lesubia, his mother, if not dead yet, was soon to die.

47

Everyone, even the lowliest of beings in the house of Alceo Jico, had to think of each of the details of her death. It was as if something in the family were about to break, then all would appear naked, showing on their bodies the exact measure of their limitations. He thought that he was no longer a son of Lesubia, he never would be again. A mother is not a mother because she conceives the son and bears him; she must conceive him and bear him even after her death. The virtues or larvae of the son become the larvae of her ashes. If Lesubia, the one who conceived and bore him deformed, died, he would die a little more. He would approach the inevitable ending like a leaf, trembling suspended in the air before falling.

His mother had repeated to him many times, tirelessly, as though trying to justify his life: "You will rise up; you will never again kneel or drag yourself along as you do now. No one will see you sleeping in your own filth, in your drooling and in the perspiration that rots you. You will go. If sometime you return to this house, you will search for my memory and you will find it to be that of the woman who kissed you for the first time on the forehead. And when hate rises in your throat, tears at your eyes and shakes your poor, crazy head, you will search for my memory and find it as that of the woman who kissed you for the first time on the forehead."

Autilo thought she told him that, or she might have told him that, or that at this moment he was hearing it from those vanishing lips. But whatever it was, finding himself condemned to innocence, he wished that the dust, the ashes of his mother, would cover him as water covers the fish. At least he would be safe from other semen, from another womb; no other woman's birthing would expose him to the light—a condensed, dark cloud, a small, dirty, molting rat.

Caima spits furiously every time she hears the ravings of Alceo Jico and says out loud, "Drunkard, drunkard!" But she thinks to herself: Lesubia has not run off with any blond policeman. A woman who has spent so many years living for her man doesn't run off just to be running off.

It isn't easy to go off one day or another and leave all that revolves around what we are . . . because everything around us is perhaps our only, our true pleasure. And so what we want to be or stop being begins in the name we give things, and this is what most flatters us deep inside. For some reason the best days of a life have been spent one after another, counted like whiplashes, communicating with the crockery and the furniture, with the walls and floors, with trees and animals, with people who have died and with those who still live, with the form of these eyes, which is something more than a simple glance; in reality it is the gaze of our heart. It is the desires and fears, spilling like mud from the warmth of the skin and the senses, filling things with emotion, that wind up being themselves, the echo and the mirror of our life. Because of this, Lesubia has not run off with any blond policeman, like that pig Alceo Jico proclaims. I am sure. But can we find ourselves certain of anything? To have gone off . . . well, to have gone off is something that she had been doing ever since she was born. In any event she wanted to. She simply has done what she wanted to, and a woman calls many things doing what she wants to. And if she really has died? Perhaps he didn't hear her sigh deeply that afternoon and, with her eyes watery and yellow, tell him: "Bring me Antino, pass me the little one, the little Egg." (The baby had no hair, not even eyebrows, so they called him the Egg—Antino, the Egg.) "I want to look at his round, sad little face." And I brought the baby to her bed and saw when Lesubia's swollen, dry lips kissed his bald little head. It is also possible that Lesubia was in the village, or farther away, in the city or much beyond that because no one knows, no one, not even her own mother, where a woman's feet can take her.

His mother had to die, so he must prepare himself for death. He will no longer be a son of Alceo Jico, nor will he ever be again. There began once more that, "A father is not a father because he engenders the son once; he must engender him even after his death. And each one of the virtues or vices of the son will be simply the spawn of his ashes." If Lesubia dies, we shall be a little more dead, more disgustingly dead. What Lesubia had said to him, what she repeated to him tirelessly, he in turn repeated to himself incessantly until the words became deformed. He asked himself, "Are they the same, or have I already changed them?" Lesubia, whom he thought of as "the woman with the black, shiny hair," told him, or might have told him— and here once more he became entangled in the black mesh of his dreams—"You will never again be lying, or kneeling, nor will you ever again drag yourself along the ground. Alceo Jico, your father, will not see you sitting as you do now in your own filth, in your drooling and in the waters that rot you." He thinks he was told that, or might have been told that.

This was the afternoon Alceo Jico arrived at the house with a young black bull. Autilo could hear the voices of the neighbors who came up to propose some business deal. Alceo Jico only said, "He is not for sale," and moved his eyes as if to say: "Some day he will not be for sale, but now, at this moment, he is, yes, he is. Now more than ever he is. Now, precisely when he is nothing, this bull is for sale; now when I do not know whether he is really mine, this bull can be sold. It is just that when they ask me and I want to say that he is for sale, I say the contrary, I say that he is not for sale, but if people would understand, there would be no problems. Because then they would say, 'Very well, we are taking him, he is ours.' However, there was not one who would say that, who would simply say, 'I am taking him, he is mine.' There was not one who would approach and lift a finger to say, 'That bull is mine; I am buying him, Alceo Jico.' But no one understands. They all think that my words say what I really want to say, but this bull not being for sale, as I have said, is not the truth of what I am thinking."

He did not think, as he was thinking that day, that some day it would not be for sale, because then he did not know, as he knows now, that a woman buried in a simple black box, in a box that he himself might have made and painted, might in this very hour be a bull, and that he would one day see himself looking through the round, infuriated eyes of a black bull.

That day he arrived tranquilly, tied the bull to the locust tree, gave him water and cut green fodder for him. When someone came to ask him if the bull were for sale, he only answered, "None of that—this bull is not for sale."

And Caima, the grandmother, said, "That bull is no bull, but a box, a black box, a long, ugly black box, simply a box to bury Lesubia." The grandmother said, "Alceo Jico has always had an easy tongue, and when he said he wouldn't return without anything, I knew that he was going to bring Lesubia's box; I knew perfectly well that Lesubia would have her box."

Since then time has passed, time as long as a river that never stops passing, time as extensive and limitless as the air . . . time that is scarcely a second, a brief fluttering of wings, a blow, something that passes, crosses, dampens us inside briefly and then blinds us with a hundred summers together, with a hundred summers weighing on our backs, until it diminishes us to a bit of streaked, reddish earth. Only a bit of earth.

Lesubia no longer existed, or Lesubia had become a black bull that wandered the fields and at night bellowed continuously, tearing up earth and grass with its hoofs. That was Lesubia—a black bull bellowing and seeking in the ground a bitter well of fury, of vengeance. She was a bull of black pitch and blood instead of a woman surrounded by the honor of her family. Because she, Lesubia, bull-woman, was lying in her own coffin, tied to all the successive days of her kin.

That day, when Lesubia grew more and more pale, as she never had been before, she stretched herself on the bed and said, almost screaming, "I don't want to die." And then everyone said that she had died. Fulvio Dínaro came with his short bird-hoppings and a big, black box over his head. He spoke to Alceo Jico—who was twisting his neck and jumping as if he had hiccoughs around his cadaver-wife, wife-yet-perhaps—putting the box in the corridor,

putting it in mid-air as though the box were made of black
smoke, placing it there amid the astonished people, who
were asking themselves who was going to be put in there
and buried, in spite of knowing that the only one who would
occupy that box was, precisely, Lesubia. He had spoken in
Alceo Jico's ear, as if it were a secret matter, of a bull-calf,
of a black bull that people knew about or said they knew
about; Fulvio Dínaro, with his eyes wide open as though
he were always astonished at something, was speaking as
if in secret, slowly, as if to convince himself of something
that he had yet to be convinced of completely. Alceo Jico
stopped for a moment, looked him up and down, and then
he went on with his hiccoughs, like a repugnant toad,
hiccoughing around that strange cadaver-wife who had
fallen to his lot in the great partitioning of divine carrion.

Alceo Jico began to formulate these, or similar reflections:

"Now the people want to know what that bull signifies.
Fulvio Dínaro said something about the bull, he referred to
his lustrous, black skin and spoke of some business deal
and, although he didn't say so, I thought that surely the
deal pertained to me since I was the only one around who
owned a bull-calf of that age and color and a cadaver-wife
that was and was not Lesubia, because that is the only form
of being and not-being in this world, a cadaver-wife ready
to be put, to be placed in that black box lined with the
blackest pitch."

Alceo Jico thought that Fulvio Dínaro had said or
suggested to him something like this:

"Although nobody really knows where that bull-calf
came from, and many don't care, that bull-calf should be
enclosed in my corral, should eat my grass and drink my
water, and now I might say some words about him, which,
although they occur to me, I would not know how to say
properly, because if not, ultimately, you, Alceo Jico, will
not be able to answer a single one of my questions, will
not be able to say whether your wife was or was not buried
in her own box. It is almost certain you will not be able

to answer that. Because of that I tell you that I can pronounce some words concerning this bull."

Alceo Jico thought that he looked at Fulvio Dínaro then
as one who looks from far away, from a distance at a thing
difficult to distinguish, whether it be a horse, a tree or
simply a patch of shade. And only after a while did he
answer.

"It is not for me to say the last word about this bull-
calf, although in truth, with respect to myself I don't think
I have ever begun to reach an understanding with you
concerning the words which in certain cases a man may
pronounce about an animal like this or any other, and
that in spite of my having to take charge of something that
must be enclosed in a box, buried forever inside something
placed there by the heart of her kinfolk."

But that day Fulvio Dínaro had other wandering
thoughts. He remembered that he had approached the house
and had said to the grandmother Caima, "Listen, I thought
that Alceo Jico had brought the bull-calf to sell and I
would have liked to trade something for it, no matter
what."

Caima, continuing to blow on the weak flame of the
hearth, had answered: "I don't understand Alceo Jico because before going to bring this bull-calf he told me, 'I will
not return without bringing something to trade for a box
for Lesubia!' And that is how it was, although I don't know
how, nor with what money he bought this bull-calf. Maybe
they gave it to him on credit, you know, because Alceo
Jico is a resourceful man. It might be because Alceo Jico,
I tell you, has a wise tongue. And if not, how do you think
he could at a given moment have on his hands a dead
woman, a box and a bull—three things no man except
Alceo Jico, in that moment, could claim as his?"

Fulvio Dínaro looked and looked at her from his dark
eyes, from his beardless face, from his incredulity. It is
difficult to mislead a man like Fulvio Dínaro with a thought
like that. A man who owns no more than an abandoned
sand mine—mused Fulvio Dínaro—suddenly, with a view

to his wife's dying, leaves his home, his land, takes the road and returns happily leading, tied to a short halter, a black bull-calf, black and shining like sun-dried blood. To a man like Fulvio Dínaro these things have only one answer. Alceo Jico did not buy that black bull-calf, he could not have bought it; he simply appropriated it, not to say openly that he had stolen it. Because, if Alceo Jico had stood up in the center of the patio in his house and shouted, cupping his hands to his mouth—"I have stolen a bull. Come and see it. I have stolen it"—nobody, nobody, it is certain, would have believed that Alceo Jico had stolen the bull-calf. At worst, people would have said, "That Alceo Jico and his nonsense; he has even sold the children's playthings to buy this bull-calf and now he comes around shouting he has stolen it—the devil with Alceo Jico."

That was what Alceo Jico had invented about his mother (Autilo was thinking) in order to say that, even dead, no-body, not he, nor his grandmother Caima, nor anybody might say whether or not she was dead. Autilo, meanwhile, strained his eyes, looking out where darkness was seizing everything.

From the kitchen came odors of young corn ears on the fire. He listened to the crackling of the green firewood, and the column of sticky smoke seemed like an arm above the roof. He watched the coals flashing between the black knobs of rock. Suddenly Caima, the grandmother, passed her old, black hand through her hair and asked something of the air, asked something nostalgically of a being who was not visible anywhere, but who, nevertheless, was present. Here, for her, was a complete, turbid, family conversation with details standing out so that one could recognize the physiognomy of all the persons who, in one manner or another, had influenced the grandmother's life. She went on saying everything slowly, between heavy puffings at the fire, as if afraid that suddenly she would have nothing more to say.

From his cot, Autilo listened patiently to all these things the grandmother spoke of, the detours she made around them and how at the end she began once more, with exactly the same words and the same personages.

He remembered now, who knows by what strange association of ideas, the things that Lura Magina once said about the world, the world she was always imagining, and where, above all, she found odors and flavors—it seemed to him after that conversation—that she would never again be able to appreciate and which, nevertheless, appeared to her in the most simple or unexpected things. And all this had nothing—absolutely nothing—to do with his mother, Lesubia, who had risen or gone down, and according to what everybody said, was dead. And grandmother Caima repeated that, dead or not, no one could ever catch up with her, the inevitable one's, footsteps because Lesubia had become like the air. Anyway, in case it had been real death (of which, according to the grandmother, it was almost possible to be certain), none of the neighbors, friends or enemies, could come and say "There is someone who says they buried her at night, erasing the moon with a black cloth, so no one would learn of her burial without a coffin, tossed into a hole like a bundle of old rags." Because, whether or not it was all true in Lesubia's case, Alceo Jico had foreseen that black bull-calf, that black-coffin-bull-calf, which saved the family from being looked upon as one looks upon trash. For nobody, that night or the following nights in the world, nobody could keep from hearing the bellowing of that black, seething coffin that tore up the earth with the fury of horns and engraved his presence forever in the throat, the eyes, the anguish of all, proclaiming that Lesubia lay dead beneath the stars, beneath the earth in her own box and in that way had not at all dishonored the Jico family. That was why what Autilo was remembering had nothing to do with Lesubia, his mother, but with Lura Magina, someone new and different, who was for him, amid the plain and simple things of his life, the strangest thing of all.

In the days of Lura, that afternoon of soft twilight, yellow fields and green-black sparks in the old kitchen—

Lura Magina seated on that small stool, combing her dirty hair with a wooden comb, had been commenting on something concerning recently sprouted fields, where the beans grew like snakes and where the beans rained down, soaking with their juice the hairy backs of red heifers that passed through, lowing and shaking their undeveloped horns happily. She said that one could see all the lifted tails and the udders still without milk and then she began to smell cow-dung, as if all the beans had changed into fresh cow-dung. She said it thus, seated and with her voice seated nearly at her feet, passing the comb again and again through her hair, and listening to something like fine grains of rice falling on her skirt, without lifting her eyes, without lifting her gaze, without lifting anything that she really might have lifted. And then she said that what she never was going to forget easily was that parcel behind Fulvio Dínaro's house, where it seemed to be raining all the year around and where the blackest and yellowest celery she had ever seen grew like savage stumps, and that she saw how a band of pigs went into the parcel and began to root there until all of those stumps were turned up, still full of sap, still covered with bitter, smelly earth, and that was when she heard Fulvio Dínaro say that all women smelled like recently pulled celery, and it seemed to her that maybe it was true because that celery rooted up by the pigs gave off a violent odor that burnt like coals.

In those days Autilo found Lura Magina's way of thinking very strange. She always seemed to be stumbling across things that were her own. Since these things never agreed —they were generally very different—and since he, at that time, paid no attention to them, she with some hidden purpose, or none whatever, seemed to give them importance and bring them up when Autilo least expected it, although he let them pass and listened to them as though he were hearing the recital of other things. But if Lura Magina insisted, he noticed that little by little he started to catch the meaning of all that she said and began to form his own image, an image of what was happening probably different from the one she, Lura Magina, felt, or not so different but at least singular.

Lura Magina dwelt frequently on those chores she knew when she was much younger. She said she remembered the boards with wooden wheels the boys made, placing on each one a candle, and all those candles wandering about in the darkness made her sad and to her appeared to be the mysterious movements of people inside their houses who dared not go out at night because those who seemed to be free of fear began a prolonged whistling from beyond the fields or amid the narrow streets of the village, those whistles sounding freer than any that could be heard from anyone's lips at any other time, and they sounded as though someone was whistling and listening to himself. And she also told about those who worked amid the warm smell of coffee, sewing coffee sacks with long needles that resembled teeth. She would enter and look at the tannery and go along between the ruined adobe walls and would see through the cracks in boards the place reserved for men, and she would squat down to look at the stream of water where everything became mingled with the color of blood. And Lura Magina told this to herself, as if trying to stimulate a secret knowledge, some mystery of her body which she had not yet been able to detect.

Meanwhile Autilo wrapped himself slowly in a mesh of sleep and, as if coming out of a tunnel, new and unexpected events began to appear before him—places where no light given off by the dirty, stinking hair of Lura Magina shone, and where Lura with her high, abundant brows and her mouth ever-tremulous like a newly extinguished lamp, submerged herself in the most shadow-saturated places, from which she came out only to take the air like a wild, lonely animal. For Autilo, each time he came out of that tunnel it was as though he were reborn, and then he saw himself with full clarity, like the sun, bathing in light and warmth all the objects that surrounded him in light and warmth.

No one dies when he should die. Everyone leaves something inconclusive behind him, and some die without even having commenced anything. Autilo was thinking this or something like it; because within himself he heard the murmur of something slowly dissolving, coming undone. But now that he scarcely moved, that everything seemed to him horizontal like his own body, he only felt inside himself those memories where Lura Magina, stretched out on a mat, exposed the full length of her thigh.

But it no longer mattered to him because he had begun the relinquishment of all that might in some manner have been able to interest him, detain him. If Lesubia, his mother, had died, if everything around him was going to disappear, it was of no importance that he himself, who had barely had time to present himself among his kind, might flee, might lose himself forever beneath a bit of earth tossed, as if by accident, into a hole opened perhaps by accident. Lamentably, everything was like that. This was the truth about what was awaiting him and, even more, he could not ask himself or anyone else, not even his grandmother Caima if he, Autilo, eldest son of Alceo Jico, would have his black box, his varnished box in the same manner in which his father proclaimed he had buried Lesubia, his mother; since those who saw her die said immediately that the woman had been buried in her own box, that the box with her body in it was carried to an empty hole and that the man who was owner of that corpse could be sure that she, who had existed, would feel, there in the earth, mistress of her own ashes.

Autilo thought this in the last days, when his eyes were no longer able to focus without great effort. If Alceo Jico had appeared with a black bull as in the case of Lesubia, if he had brought another animal like that one, tied with a short halter, another one with brilliant, lustrous skin, it is very possible that the neighbors would have risen from their beds and would have surrounded him again, asking things of no consequence to them and pondering fantastic projects about an animal they could never really possess and that no one, not even Alceo Jico himself, would dare to utilize other than as envoy of the powers that are hidden in the night and which that bull-woman represented with the tremendous force of her presence. But if Autilo died, his body, after being wound in the sheets that his mother had set aside so long ago for the purpose, would be sent into the ground with no other ceremony.

This was during Autilo's last night, nearly at dawn, when death, like a hawk of ice, brushed his forehead. The shadow of Alceo Jico was projected in sinister form against the walls, mid his agitation it could be seen walking in a squat or giving little hops. From time to time he moaned, and the shadow, turned in upon itself, became a ball on the ground.

The moon, like a crystal fruit, fell from the top of the blue bowl, and the patio seemed to be covered with flour. A rooster tied to a perch shook his wings and began to crow sonorously. Alceo Jico jumped to his feet, ran to the rooster and took it in his hands, stroking the animal's head with heavy abandon. The rooster had a red, bald head and sought nervously, like an eel, to escape from between the crusted fingers of Alceo Jico.

Then the grandmother Caima appeared in the door to Autilo's room and, standing tranquilly with her thin hands over her breast, announced in a long-suffering, maternal voice: "He is dead."

It was no more than that, but it was enough for Alceo Jico to feel a vacuum surrounding him, and he slowly squeezed the reddish head of the rooster which, with a brief squawk, burst between his fingers, covering his hand with fresh blood. Alceo Jico then thought and said aloud, "He hasn't died yet." But the air already resounded with its thousands of birds and the sun in the east resembled a young, wild mushroom.

Ruben Bonifaz Nuno

Author of six volumes of poetry, a graduate in law from the University of Mexico and holder (1951-1952) of a Rockefeller Foundation grant, this young Mexican was born in Veracruz in 1923. Among his publications are *La muerte del angel, Imagenes* and *El manto y la coronoa.*

The Flower

Sometimes
a flower appears on the smoothest
surface of the river.
It senses the air a-tremble to receive it,
it unpuzzles the light, and in a profound,
infinite gesture, it unfolds.
Vessel of snow, tender, most perfect,
it is the center of everything. Necessary
to the water that embraces it,
and to the sky that touches it
and is born from it as from a fountain.
It is the flower of a single instant: futureless
and without past, forming among its petals
the abyss of an immobile present.

The soft,
the silent, primitive womb
of the water conceives it
in the unmixed solitude of the riverbed.
And the place which knows movement
only from the shudder
that shakes the water—as if remembering
the wind passing above—and feeling the anguish
of the unconscious rubbing of the fish
against the icy edge of an hour,
protests with an obscure quivering:

It knows nothing, yet feels the flower seed
surging like a pulse beat
in its solitary entrails.

Later,
engulfed in its opaque wrappings,
the flower germinates mysteriously,
suffers patiently and prepares itself.
Greenly there extends between flower and bed
the link of a stem which feeds
and retains it;
which kindles in the future flower the
urge of an angel in chains that would
fly; sad canal that gives life
to be transcended, that, defeated,
is broken finally when, near maturity,
the buoyant flower slowly
rises tranquilly to touch the air.

Then
the flower goes, shedding its purity.
One petal after another reaches
for the air's embrace, the precise embrace,
and in surrendering all, synthesizes
the beauty of everything and transforms it.
The lisping love of the now-forgotten
riverbed, and the other love now discovered,
create of love the newly opened flower
immobile. Eternal in the inconceivable
instant. Clear, dead, alone.
Clear in the fullness of beauty;
dead in the solitude, for it does not pass away,
alone in its stillness, it is perfection.

La flor

A veces
aparece una flor en la más limpia

superficie del río.
Siente que el aire tiembla al recibirla,
adivina la luz, y en un profundo
ademán infinito se desnuda.
Barca nevada, tierna, perfectísima,
es el centro de todo. Necesaria
al agua que la ciñe,
y al cielo que la toca
y en ella nace como de una fuente.
Es la flor de un instante: sin futuro
y sin pasado, forma entre sus pétalos
el abismo de un presente inmóvil.

El blando,
el silencioso vientre primitivo
del agua la concibe
en la sencilla soledad del cauce.
Y el lugar que conoce el movimiento
sólo por el escalofrío
que estremece las aguas—si recuerdan
que arriba pasa el viento—y por la angustia
del inconsciente roce de los peces,
en el filo de hielo de una hora
gime con un sacudimiento oscuro:
No sabe nada, y siente que ha brotado
el germen de la flor, como un latido
en sus entrañas solitarias.

Más tarde,
sumida en sus opacas envolturas,
la flor germina misteriosamente,
sufre pacientemente y se prepara.
Glauco se tiende entre la flor y el cauce
el vínculo de un tallo, que la nutre
y la retiene;
que enciende en la futura flor el ansia
de un ángel en cadenas, que intentara
volar; triste canal que da la vida
para ser superado, que vencido
se rompe al fin, cuando casi madura

la flor ligera, lentamente,
sube tranquila hasta tocar el aire.

Entonces
va la flor desvistiendo su pureza.
Un pétalo tras otro va tendiendo
al abrazo del aire, al más exacto;
y al entregarse toda sintetiza
la belleza de todo y la transforma.
El balbuciente amor del ya olvidado
cauce, y el otro amor ya descubierto,
hacen de amor la flor recién abierta
que está inmóvil. Eterna en el instante
inconcebible. Clara, muerta, sola.
Clara en la plenitud de la belleza;
muerta en la soledad, pues no transcurre,
y sola en su quietud, porque es perfecta.

JOAQUIN PASOS

Two volumes of verse represent the published work of this young Nicaraguan poet, who died in 1947 at the age of thirty-two.

Elegy of the Bird

Oh, wild and sweet bird, eater of fruits,
return me the green wine of your elusive plumage,
spill it in the shouting-drunken air,
stir it in my soul with your naked beak!
May the goddess who supplies fields with young birds
pour over my blood this rustic liquor,
may your color circulate through my body,
nest of wild birds, ah, dead birds.

But the sweet moon, she who listens to
the silent songs of tongueless birds,
sees in my heart as in a limpid well
the corpse of your soul floating like a petal.
With your unseeing gaze, deep as a nail
you fix the vertex of this sad moment
while a rustle of dry feathers sounds in the air
and the broken wings are rent by sleep.
Rise, bird, rise to the utmost branch,
the one that bids the world good-by, door to the heavens;
fling your wild flesh, garlanded with feathers,
fling your sweet flesh, perfumed with fruits.
Towards you these two hands, these hands await
the palmful of jungle blood in your body
to show to the world like a resplendent jewel,
like the best, the best of the harvest.
Over these tears of mine extinguish your flight,
drown in sobs your clarion cry,

and may your warm body rest forever
in my sorrow which forms your nest.

Elegia de la pájara

¡Oh loca y dulce pájara comedora de frutas,
devuélveme el vino verde de tu plumaje esquivo,
derrámalo en el aire emborrachado a gritos,
agítalo en mi alma con tu pico desnudo!
Que la diosa que surte los campos de aves nuevas
vierta sobre mi sangre este licor agreste,
que tu color circule a través de mi cuerpo
nido de locos pájaros ¡ ay! pájaros muertos.

Pero la dulce luna, la que escucha los cantos
silenciosos de las aves sin lengua,
vea en mi corazón como en un pozo límpido
el cadáver de tu alma flotando como un pétalo.
Con tu mirada ciega y honda como un clavo
estás fijando el vértice de este momento triste,
mientras suena en el aire rumor de plumas secas
y las alas quebradas se desgajan con sueño.
Sube, pájara, sube a la postrera rama,
la que despide al mundo, el puerto de los cielos;
lanza tu carne loca florecida de plumas,
lanza tu carne dulce perfumada de frutas.
Hacia tí estas dos manos, estas manos que esperan
el manojo de sangre de selva de tu cuerpo
para mostrarlo al mundo como una joya fúlgida,
como lo mejor, lo mejor de la cosecha.
Sobre este llanto mío que se apague tu vuelo,
que se ahogue en sollozos el clarín de tu grito,
y que tu cuerpo tibio descanse para siempre
en mi dolor que tiene la forma de tu nido.

Augusto Monterroso

This Guatemalan writer was born in Tegucigalpa, capital city of Honduras, in 1922. The author of three short story collections, all published in Mexico, Monterroso's work has been called "intelligent, witty, ironical, paradoxical." In "First Lady" he employs his talent for satire as a weapon of social protest.

First Lady

My husband says it's just my foolishness, she thought, but what he wants is for me to stay at home, working myself to death the way I did before. And he isn't going to have his way. The rest may be afraid of him, but I am not. As if I hadn't helped him when we were still having hard times! And why shouldn't I be able to recite if I like to? The fact that he's President now should make him realize that instead of being an obstacle, I can help him more that way. It's just that men, Presidents or not, are stupid. Besides, I'm not going to go around like a fool, reciting anywhere, but only at official functions or at benefits. Why not, if there's nothing wrong with it?

There was nothing wrong with it. She finished bathing and went into her bedroom. While she combed her hair she saw in the mirror behind her shelves full of disordered books—novels, poetry. She thought about some of them and how much she liked them—anthologies of the thousand best universal poems in which she had inserted slips of paper to mark the most beautiful selections ("To Laugh Weeping," "The Head of the Rabbi," "Tropic," "To a Mother"). Good heavens! Where did they find so many themes? Soon there wouldn't be enough room in the house to hold the books. But even if one didn't read them all, they made the best inheritance.

On her dressing table were several copies of the

evening's program. If she only dared to give a recital all alone. Up to now she hadn't organized one, out of modesty. But she knew, anyway, that she would be the principal figure.

This time it was a reunion prepared somewhat hurriedly for the Student Breakfast. Somebody had noticed that the children in the schools were a little bit underfed, and some of them fainted in the morning, perhaps when the teacher was at his very best. At first they attributed it to indigestion, later to an epidemic of worms (Ministry of Sanitation) and only at the last, during one of his frequent insomnia-ridden nights did the Director-General of Education suspect, vaguely, that it might be due to hunger.

When the Director-General called a goodly number of parents together, most were loudly indignant at this intimation of their poverty, and, out of pride before the others, rejected the idea. But when the meeting ended, a number of them individually approached the Director and admitted that on occasions, not always of course, they sent their children to school with empty stomachs. The Director was startled to find his suspicions confirmed and decided it was necessary to do something immediately. Luckily, he recalled that the President had been a schoolmate, and he made arrangements to go and see him as soon as possible. He did not regret his decision. The President received him most pleasantly, probably with much more cordiality than he would have displayed in a less elevated position. So that when he began, "Mr. President . . . ," the other laughed and told him: "Forget that nonsense about Mr. President and tell me straight out what you're here for." And, still laughing, the President obliged him to sit down with a slight pressure on the shoulder. The President was in good humor. But the Director knew that despite the back-slapping, things weren't the same as when they went to school together, or even the same as two years ago when they still drank together with friends in The Danube. At any rate, it was obvious that he was beginning to feel at ease in office. (As the President himself had said, raising a forefinger at a recent dinner at the home of his parents and glowing with the warm approval of his relatives and companions-at-arms: "In the beginning one feels strange; but you can get used to anything.")

"Well, then, what brings you here?" he insisted. I'll bet you're having trouble in the Ministry."

"Well, if you want to know the truth, yes."

"You see!" the President said triumphantly, verifying his own sagacity.

"But, if you'll pardon me, I didn't come about that; I'll tell you about it some other day. Look, in order to not waste your time, I'll tell you right off. There have been a number of cases of children fainting from hunger in the schools, and I'd like to see what we can do. I prefer to tell you straight off because it's stupid to stall around. Besides, it's better that *I* tell you because there are plenty of people who might come and tell you I'm not doing anything. My idea is that you could authorize me to raise some money and found a sort of semi-official milk distribution program."

"You aren't going Communist on me, are you?" the other stopped him, letting out a guffaw. He really was in excellent humor. The Director laughed heartily, too, and warned him jokingly to be careful because he was in fact reading a little book about Marxism. "Don't let the Director of Police see you or you'll be in trouble," the President replied without ceasing to laugh. After exchanging four of five more ingenious phrases on the same theme, the President told him that the plan sounded good, and that he should see who he could get the money from, that he could say the President was in agreement, and that perhaps the UN Children's Fund might provide a little more milk. "The gringos have milk to burn," he affirmed at last, rising and putting an end to the interview.

"Oh, look," he added when the Director was already at the door. "If you want to, talk to my wife about helping you; she likes those things."

The Director said, "Fine, I'll talk to her right away."

However, this depressed him more than anything else because he did not like working with women, worse yet, with women in official positions. Most of them were strange, vain, difficult, and one had to go around all the time being courteous, preoccupying oneself to be sure they were always seated, and getting nervous when, for any reason, one had to say no to them. Incidentally, he did not know her very well. But it was best to interpret the President's suggestion as an order.

When he spoke to her, she accepted unhesitatingly. How could he have any doubts? Not only would she help him by spreading the word among her friends, but she, personally, would work enthusiastically, taking part, for example, in the reunions that were organized.

"I can recite," she told him. "I've always been an enthusiast, you know." What luck, she thought, to find this opportunity. But at the same time she felt remorse for her thought, fearing that God would punish her selfishness. Poor little things, she thought rapidly in order to placate the heavens and elude punishment.

She said aloud, "Poor little creatures. And how often do they faint?"

The Director explained patiently to her that the same ones did not faint periodically, but sometimes it would be one and then another, and that the best thing would be to find a way to serve breakfast to the greatest possible number. They would have to establish an organization to gather funds.

"Of course," she agreed. "And what shall we call it?"

"How do you like 'Student Breakfast'?" asked the Director.

She passed her hand over the program, a rectangular piece of satinized paper, elegantly printed:

1. Preliminary words by Mr. Hugo Miranda, Director General of Education of the Ministry of Public Education.

2. "Barcarole" from Tales of Hoffman (*Offenbach*), *by a group of students from the Fourth of July school.*

3. Three waltzes (F. Chopin), by Rene Elgueta, student of the National Conservatory of Music.

4. "Motives of the Wolf" (Ruben Dario), by Her

Excellency, Mme. Dona Eulalia Fernández de River
Martinez, First Lady of the Republic.

　　5. *"Skies of My Homeland" (national composer*
Federico Diaz), with the author at the piano.

　　6. *National Anthem.*

She thought it was fine. Although perhaps there was
too much music and too little recitation.

"Do you like what I am going to recite?" she asked
her husband.

"As long as you don't forget the lines halfway through
and make a fool of yourself," he replied. Although he was
in bad humor, he was incapable of seriously opposing her.
"Really, I don't know why you got mixed up in this
stupidity. It seems you don't know what nuisances the boys
are. Right away they're going to start making jokes about
you. But once you get something in your head nobody can
get it out."

They can't see a wife taking any initiative, she mused,
without making objections and trying to give her a complex.

"How could I forget it?" she said aloud, rising to look
for a handkerchief. "I've known it since I was a child.
What I don't like is that I have a little bit of a cold. But
I think it's just nerves. Whenever I have something important to do I'm always afraid of getting sick and I start
thinking—I'm going to catch a cold, I'm going to catch a
cold—until I really do catch one. Yes, indeed. It must be
nerves. The proof is that afterwards it goes away."

Brusquely facing the mirror, she raised her arms and
tested her voice:

The man-n-n- who has a hear-r-rt of lilies-s-s-s
a cheru-u-u-bic sou-u-u-l, tongue celestial-l-l-l-l
the min-n-n-nimal and gentle Francis of Ass-i-i-i-i-isi
iswith

　　　　a rudeand

　　　　　　snarlingan

　　　　　　　　imal.

She pronounced "gentull." It was good to lengthen the accented syllables. But one didn't always know which they were unless they carried an orthographic accent. But anyway the important thing was to have feeling because when one doesn't have feeling the rules don't help a bit.

> *The man*
> *The man who has*
> *The man who has a heart*
> *The man who has a heart of lilies.*

When she arrived at the school it was still too early. She felt disappointed because there were only a few people occupying the seats. But, she thought, everybody always arrives late. When are we ever going to break that habit? On the small stage, behind an improvised curtain, the children of the Fourth of July school were practicing the "Barcarole" in low voices. The professor of music was giving them the A with a small, silvered pitch pipe that sounded only that very serious note. Seeing her there, watching them with a smile, he gave her a brief nod of the head and stopped moving his hands. But out of diffidence, or in order not to appear too servile, or because he really wasn't, he did not interrupt the practice. She was grateful because she was reviewing her poem mentally, and if they interrupted her she would have to pick up the thread from the beginning. As if she were really using her throat, she cleared it every five or six lines, despite the fact that she knew she only irritated it more each time—just like the teacher whose students told him his eye was bloodshot, so he started rubbing it until it became so bloodshot that they couldn't stop laughing. How strange obsessions are! What made her angriest was the certainty that the rawness in her throat would all disappear as soon as her number was over. Yes, indeed. But it was bothersome, meanwhile, to think that her voice was going to crack in the middle of the recitation.

The truth is that it would be stupid to be afraid of the audience. Theoretically, if her offering did not please them, it would be due to the fact that people in general are very ignorant and don't know how to appreciate poetry. They still had a long way to go. But precisely for that reason she was willing to take advantage of every occasion to introduce good verses to them and disclose her gifts as a declaimer.

"But, madame," the Director-General reproached her anxiously when he arrived, perspiring. "I was going to come by for you. It is not good that you have come alone."

She looked at him understandingly and calmed him courteously. Since she had become the First Lady, she rejoiced whenever she had the opportunity to demonstrate that she was a modest person, possibly more modest than anyone else in the world. She had even studied in the mirror an enchanting smile and glance which signified more or less, "How could it occur to you? Do you imagine that just because I am the wife of the President I have become presumptuous?" But the Director thought, instead, that she was treating him with irony. Depressed, he began to talk erratically of this and that. As soon as the other artists began to arrive and surround her, he took advantage of the opportunity to withdraw. Afterwards he could be seen fatuously giving orders and making arrangements, in accordance with the principle that if one doesn't do things oneself, no one else will.

He only drew near her again to tell her, "Prepare yourself, madame. We are about to begin."

Because he had a certain amount of experience, the Director slowly explained:

"We are gathered here, moved by a lofty spirit of human solidarity. There are many undernourished children. This is a problem which the government was the first to lament because, as the President has told me personally when he called me in to point out the situation, it is necessary to do something for these children in the interest of the high destiny of our native land. You must move consciences, move heaven and earth, move hearts in favor of this noble crusade. Already a number of persons from all strata of society have offered their disinterested aid. Our North American friends from that noble and generous nation, which we might justifiably call the larder of the world, have promised to make a new sacrifice of cans of powdered milk. Our task was modest in its beginnings, but we are disposed not to omit any effort to convert this not only into a real and concrete fact of the present but also into a stimulating example for future generations.

"We also have the great pride of counting on the aid of the First Lady of the Republic whose exquisite art we shall have the honor of appreciating within a few brief instants. Her generously maternal instincts moved her to the point of tears when she learned of the misfortune of these children who, because of the alcoholism of their fathers, or because of the neglect of their mothers, or for both reasons cannot enjoy the sacred institution of breakfast in their modest home. Their health and the advantages of instruction, which the Ministry that we are honored to represent this evening is determined to impart to them, in the conviction that books and only books will resolve the secular problems which the country faces, are imperiled."

After the applause the girls of the Fourth of July school sang with their customary sweetness the la, lala, lalalalala, lalalalala, lala of the "Barcarole." The pianist anxiously fidgeted before attacking his waltzes which, like so many other things in different regions of the globe that day, began and ended with happiness.

The First Lady inclined her head, mentally saying thank you. She clasped her hands and contemplated them a moment, waiting for the necessary atmosphere.

Soon she felt that through her words, St. Francis of Assisi came peeping forth into the world, minimal and gentle, taking the form of the most humble being on earth. But immediately the illusion of humility disappeared because other words, inexplicably linked with the first ones, altered his aspect until he became an angry man. She felt he had to be that way and no other because he was calling to account a wolf whose fangs had taken a horrible toll of shepherds, flocks and any living thing that got in his way. Yes, indeed! Her voice trembled, and tears formed at the precise instant that the saint told the wolf not to be bad.

Why didn't he stop going around creating terror among the peasants, and did he perhaps come from the Inferno? But immediately afterward one could almost see tranquility flowing from her lips when the animal, not without having thought about it for a while, followed the saint to the village. Everybody marveled to see him so tame that even a child could feed him from his hand. The words came sweetly and gently then, and she thought that the wolf could also feed the child so he wouldn't faint in school from hunger.

But she felt anguish again because in one of St. Francis' careless moments, the wolf returned to the woods to exterminate the country people and their flocks. Here her voice acquired a tone of implacable condemnation. She raised and lowered it as necessary without remembering a thing about her cold or those accursed nerves of preceding days. She was wrapped in a soothing sensation of security— security because it was obvious that the audience listened to her, strongly impressed by the brutality of the wild beasts.

But she knew that in a moment the roles would change and the wolf would turn from accused into accuser when St. Francis, with his customary confidence, once again went to look for him. However, much as one didn't want to, one had to take the side of the wolf, whose words were easily interpreted. ("Yes, very nice, isn't it? There I was, all tamed, eating whatever they felt like tossing me, licking everybody's hands like a lamb. Meanwhile, men in their homes delivered themselves over to envy, lust, rage and made war on each other. The weak lost and the wicked won.") She said the words "weak" and "wicked" in such different tones that nobody could doubt in the least that she was on the side of the first group. And she felt certain that her recital was a success because one really became indignant before acts so base that they made those of the wolf seem harmless by comparison. After all, an animal is not a rational being.

Finally, she approached the moment when she knew that now, now, now, the words must come from her throat not too strong or too tender, not furious or gentle, but pregnant with desperation and affliction because the saint

could feel no other way when he admitted the justice of
what the wolf said and directed himself at the last to
Our-r-r-r Father-r-r-r who ar-r-r-rt in heaven-n-n-n.

She remained some seconds with her arms uplifted.
Perspiration ran in threads between her breasts and down
her back. She heard them applauding. She lowered her
hands. She arranged her skirt unobtrusively and bowed
modestly. The public, after all, was not so stupid. But it was
costing her a real effort to push them toward poetry. That
was what she was thinking, little by little. While she shook
the hands of those congratulating her, she felt a sweet and
delicate sense of superiority. When a humble lady, approaching to greet her, told her how nice it had been, she
almost embraced her. Restraining herself, she asked instead,
"Did you like it?" In truth, she was no longer thinking about
her recital but about how nice it would be to organize another function, in a larger hall, perhaps in a real theater, in
which she alone would take the responsibility for the entire
program. The bad thing about these programs was that the
musicians bored people, and what was worse, the next day's
newspapers would praise them as much as they would
applaud her.

At the door of her house she invited the Director-
General and two or three friends to have a whisky "to
celebrate." She wanted to prolong the conversation about
her triumph a little while more. If only her husband were
there to hear what they told her, to convince him that they
weren't just her ideas. How well everything had turned
out! But how much was collected?

The Director-General informed her very elaborately
that they had profits of $7.50.

"So little?" she said.

He thought, bitterly, but said, optimistically, that it
wasn't bad for the first time. They had lacked publicity.

"No," she said. "I think the hall was too small."

"Well, of course," he said, "you are right about that."

"What shall we do?" she asked. "Something has to be
done to help those poor children."

"Well," he said, "the idea is to keep going ahead. We

have to organize something more serious. I think that if we can count on your help . . ."

"Yes, we can get a theater. I am going to recite, you see. But it has to be a big theater. You saw what happens when one makes an effort preparing everything and in the end collects almost nothing. Anyway, I'm going to talk to my husband. He is always urging me to recite. He's my greatest stimulus. Imagine, people really want to hear poetry. If you could know the emotion I felt when a lady who didn't even know me told me how much she liked it. I think a poetry recital would be a success. What do you think?" she said.

"Of course," he said. "People like it a great deal."

"I'm worried though," she went on, "about how little we collected today. How would it be if I gave you a hundred pesos so it doesn't come out so badly? I want to help so much. I think that little by little we'll come out all right."

He said, of course, little by little they would come out all right.

Jose Guillermo Ros Zanet

As a student of ancient and present-day American Indian civilizations, this young Panamanian poet is a fervent advocate of "a poetry of the Americas." He was born in the town of David, in 1930, studied medicine at the University of Panama, and has published one book of poems.

Poem of Contemporary Days and Love

Not burnt, nor coffined,
but laid upon the soil . . .
EDITH SITWELL: THE TOMB OF AGAMEMNON

The bulls, kneeling and absolute,
as if they were awaiting cities and millenniums.

To the deepest things
the roots of the forest or the timber return,
as if seeking a man immersed,
alone and kneeling.

And on the corners, separated
by a lean year for herds,
I come to wait for my girl and her love,
as if there would never be another way
than to love at the edge of the awaitings,
or on the brink of our hardest, self-inflicted death.

Now more than ever I understand
the mourning of the children
who walked toward death without shoes;
the nocturnal families kneeling
at the edge of ruins and of cold;
the tables, as night came on,
without bread, without light, and without cloths;

77

the doors that waited in vain
to be touched by loving hands
and not by bullets and warriors;
the innocent condemned who died
of jails, shadows and dampness;
the gray uselessness of certain votive offerings;
the roads that cancelled themselves in emptiness,
with no one, with no sandals of obscure walkers;
the disinhabited armor;
the monastic silence
of cities with destruction weighing upon them.
Now more than ever I understand.
Now more than ever I understand
with my heart more lonely, kneeling;
as if we walk
toward death with a hard mask
and an alien voice;
with scarcely room for the body;
without light, without bread; without crucifixes and candles
    lighting us;
with scarcely time to die in peace,
sordidly, obscurely kneeling.

Poema de los días y del amor contemporaneos

Los toros reclinados y totales
como si fuesen a esperar ciudades y milenios.

A las cosas más hondas
retornan las raíces del bosque o la madera,
como a buscar un hombre inmerso
y solo y reclinado.

Y en las esquinas, divididas
por mal año de bestias,
vengo a esperar la novia y sus amores;
como si no quedara jamás otro camino

que amar al pie de las esperas,
o al borde de la muerte más dura que nos damos.

Hoy más que nunca entiendo
el luto de los niños
que caminaron para morir sin sus zapatos;
las nocturnas familias reclinadas
al borde del escombro y del frío;
las mesas que anochecieron
sin pan, sin luz y sin manteles;
las puertas que esperaron en vano
ser tocadas por manos amorosas
y no por balas y guerreros;
los reos inocentes que murieron
de cárcel, sombras y humedades;
la ineficacia gris de ciertos exvotos;
los caminos que fueron cerrándose sin nada,
sin nadie, sin sandalias de oscuros caminantes;
las armaduras sin que nada las habite;
el monacal silencio
de ciudades con la destrucción a cuestas.
Hoy más que nunca entiendo.
Hoy más que nunca entiendo
con mi corazón más solo reclinado;
como si camináramos
para morir con una dura máscara
y la voz extranjera;
con sitio apenas para el cuerpo;
sin luz; sin pan; sin crucifijos y cirios alumbrándonos;
con tiempo apenas para bien morir,
malamente, oscuramente reclinados.

Otto Raul Gonzalez

Five books of verse have come from the pen of this Guatemalan poet: *Voz y voto del geranio*, *A fuego lento*, *Joven camarada* (a translation of poems by Stephen Spender), *Sombras era*, and *Viento claro*. He was born in Guatemala City in 1921, and has traveled in the Soviet Union and China as well as in Europe and Central America.

To the Scavenger

Who would mold the sordid protest of your eyes
in hard stone flung by volcanoes,
who would mold the nostalgia of your hands,
your mean stature
of cypress in twilight,
of abandoned, aimless cypress?

Your decayed trunk,
your mutilated branches
of desolate, vegetal man,
and the ruin of your shoulders
defeated by the moss and rubbish?

Who would mold your bitter substance
of fish of old salt-corroded silver,
of fish tarnished in the surf?

Who would mold your history-less steps,
your soundless steps upon the spongy earth
of that dark isle
where the crematory holds out its beacon?

On what plaque your name,
and of what metal the sword
that daily wounds your rationed dream?

Must I learn a statuary of tears and mud
and break fingernails to see the stone
in the solid quarries of hunger and misery?

Al basurero

Quién plasmara la sórdida protesta de sus ojos
en dura piedra arrojada por volcanes,
quién plasmara la nostalgia de sus manos,
su roñosa estatura
de ciprés en el crepúsculo,
de abandonado ciprés a la deriva.

Su carcomido tronco,
sus mutiladas ramas
de hombre vegetal y desolado,
y la derrota de sus hombros
vencido por el musgo y los desechos.

Quién plasmara su amarga sustancia
de pez de sal y plata viejas,
de pez oscurecido en la resaca.

Quién plasmara sus pasos sin historia,
sus pasos sin sonido sobre la tierra fofa
de esa oscura isla
donde avanza su faro el crematorio.

¿En qué placa su nombre
y en qué metal la espada
que hiere diariamente su sueño racionado?

Habría que aprender una estatuaria de lágrimas y lodo
y quebrarse las uñas para buscar la piedra
en las sólidas canteras del hambre y la miseria.

ADALBERTO ORTIZ

Two volumes of poetry, one volume of verse, a novel, and a number of articles in reviews and periodicals represent this author's published work. His novel, *Juyungo*, has been translated into French, German and Czech. Born in 1914 in the town of Esmeraldas, Ortiz has traveled widely in the Western Hemisphere and has served in his country's diplomatic service in Mexico and Paraguay.

The News

Along with four whiskies and plain water
and twenty-two cold beers
arrived my doctor, who had wandered through Europe.
He came back in a third-class cabin
taking advantage of his lengthy fellowship.
Actually, he had seen a lot of the world.
He told us how the stupendous Nordic blondes
abolished sexual prejudices and complexes,
interesting themselves a great deal these days
in "the ardent men of the South,"
especially the dark ones.
He told us how in Spain, in France and in Italy
people have no great affection for bathing.
It happened that a fellow lodger in Madrid
wrote his mother who lived in Logroño:
"Mother:
There are two crazy South Americans here
who take showers every day."
The resigned lady answered by return mail:
"If they have that naive mania, imitate them;
it may be that God wills it, my son."
Between drinks that came and glasses that went
he told us of his tours of the Louvre, and said:
"There it was, boy. What a jewel the Mona Lisa is!"

Then he asked the waiter for two orders of roasted *chifles*
and, emptying the chile jar, he ate them all himself.
There's nothing like one's country after so many years!
He went on talking of the high or low cost of living
in those nations and cities
and interpreted, in his way, European politics.
And above all, just before a most pompous and singular toast,
he told me very quietly
Lulu had died.

La noticia

Entre cuatro whiskies sin gaseosa
y veintidos cervezas congeladas,
llegó mi médico que había andado por Europa.
Vino en tercera con cabina
disfrutando de su larga beca.
En efecto, él había visto tanto mundo.
Nos contó cómo las estupendas rubias nórdicas
abolieron los prejuicios sexuales y complejos,
interesándose mucho en estos días
por "los ardientes hombres del Sur",
especialmente los morenos.
Nos contó cómo en España, en Francia y en Italia
las gentes no tienen gran afecto por el baño.
Así, pues, un compañero del mismo pensionado en Madrid,
escribió a su vieja que vivía en Logroño:
"Madre:
Aquí hay dos locos sudamericanos
que se duchan diariamente".
La resignada señora contestó sobre la marcha:
"Si tienen esa ingenua manía, imítalos,
que sea lo que Dios quiera, hijo mío".
Entre copa que venía y copa que se iba,
nos contó de sus andanzas por el Louvre, y dijo:
—Ahí tenés, cholito. ¡Qué alhaja ha sido la Gioconda!

Luego pidió al mozo dos platos de chifles con hornado
y vaciando el ajicero, se los devoró solito.
¡No hay como la Patria de uno, después de tantos años!
Siguió hablando de lo cara o lo barata que es la vida
en aquellas naciones y ciudades
e interpretó, a su manera, la política europea.
Y sobre todo, previo un brindis muy pomposo y singular,
me informó muy quedamente
que Lulú había muerto.

Augusto Roa Bastos

For his novel *Hijo de hombre*, Augusto Roa Bastos was awarded the 1960 prize for an imaginative prose work by the city of Buenos Aires. His other published works include a collection of short stories and a volume of poetry. Born in Asuncion in 1918, he served as a war correspondent in London, France and North Africa during World War II. The war in the Chaco, referred to in the following story, was fought (1932-1935) over a disputed boundary between Bolivia and Paraguay at the cost of one million lives.

The Excavation

The first movement of earth occurred about three yards behind him. At first it did not seem at all alarming: it was probably a soft seam of the upper earth. The shadows became only a tiny bit more dense in the narrow passage where a man could only squirm backward or forward on his belly. He could not stop now. He kept digging forward with the tin plate that served as his digging tool. The increasing dampness impregnating the hard earth encouraged him. The gully could not be far away now, four or five yards at the most, or some twenty-five more days of labor to the liberating opening beyond the river.

Alternating in continuous four-hour shifts, six prisoners were pushing the excavation forward some eight inches a day. They could have gone faster, but the amount of work was limited by the possibility of removing the earth in the waste can without its being noticed. They had abstained from utilizing the can which entered and left twice a day, and so won for themselves a few inches more of storage space for smuggling out excavated earth.

The civil war had ended six months earlier. The digging had been under way for four months. Meanwhile, some seventeen of the eighty-nine political prisoners jammed together in that inhospitable cell, den, privy—where in normal times no more than eight or ten common prisoners had ever entered—had died from various causes.

Of the seventeen prisoners who had possessed the foolish notion of dying, nine had been carried off by assorted diseases contracted either before or after their imprisonment, four by the urgent compulsions of the torture chamber, two by the torrential current of galloping consumption. Two had committed suicide by opening their veins, one with the tongue of his belt buckle, the other with a plate whose edge he had sharpened against the wall. The plate now served as the tunnel-digging tool.

These statistics rule the lives of the unfortunates—their hopes and despairs; their anxieties, calloused but still sensitive; their thirst, hunger, pains, smells; the hatred flaming in their blood, in their eyes, like those wax-fed butterflies that a mere hundred yards away shone in the cathedral before the images.

The only breath came from the still-blind hole, still nonexistent but growing like a child in the bellies of those anxiously waiting—the pure odor of liberty, a fresh, shining breeze amid the excrement. And there one could touch, in a sort of imminence achieved by vertigo, all that lay beyond that black maw. That was what the prisoners felt when they dug earth with the tin plate in the narrow night of the tunnel.

A new cave-in buried his legs, this time up to the small of his back. He wanted to move, to draw up his trapped extremities, but he could not. Suddenly, while pain grew with dull stitches in his flesh, in the bones of his buried legs, he became aware of exactly what was happening. It had not been a mere soft streak. It was probably a wedge of earth, a thick block that reached to the surface. Probably an entire foundation was sinking into the flaw provoked by the cave-in.

He had no recourse but to keep digging ahead—to dig with all his strength, without pause, to dig with the plate, with his fingernails as far he could. Perhaps there were not five yards still to go, perhaps not twenty-five days still separated him from the rescuing aperture in the river bank.

Perhaps it was less—only a few inches, a few more minutes of deep scratching. He became a frantic mole. He felt the earth becoming more and more moist. As the quantity of air diminished, he grew more animated. Hope increased in the same measure as his asphyxia. A bit of tepid clay between his fingers caused him to break out with a cry almost of happiness. But he was so absorbed in his emotion, so enveloped by the maddening darkness of the tunnel, that he could not realize it was not the nearness of the river, not its infiltration, that had dampened the mud but his own blood flowing from beneath his fingernails and from fingertips wounded by the earth. In the epilogue of the fatal duel that had started long ago, the dense and impenetrable earth was wearing him out effortlessly and was now beginning to swallow him alive and warm.

Suddenly the earth seemed to give way a bit. He clawed in the emptiness. Like a stone, he remained behind, strangling on the air. He tried to advance, but now his legs formed an irremediable part of the block that had slid down on them. He no longer even felt them. He felt only the asphyxia. He was drowning in a solid, dark river. He stopped moving, stopped the useless struggle. The torment slowly changed into an inexplicable delight. He began to remember. He remembered that other subterranean mine in the Chaco War a long time ago, a time that now seemed to him fabulous. He recalled it clearly, nevertheless, in all its details.

On the Gondra front the war had bogged down. For six months Paraguayans and Bolivians, embedded face to face in their impregnable positions, exchanged fire and insults obstinately. There was no more than a fifty-yard distance between them. During the lulls on nights that melancholy forgetfulness made cruelly memorable, they exchanged music and songs of their respective countries instead of machine-gun fire.

The entire high plateau, rocky and desolate, descended with the plaintive pull of the *cuecas;* an entire race forged of copper and punishment came down from its cosmic platform into the voracious dust of the trenches. And there also descended from the great rivers, from the immense Paraguayan forests, from the hearts of its people—who were also absurdly, cruelly persecuted—the polkas and *guaranias*, mingling, fraternizing with that other melodious breath that rose from death. It happened that way because Americans had to continue dying, killing each other, in order that certain things might be expressed correctly in terms of statistics and markets, exchange and proper spoliation, with exact ciphers and numbers in the bulletins of international rapine.

It was during one of these pauses that Perucho Rodi, engineering student, dutiful son and excellent brother, suave and handsome with his dark skin and green eyes, along with fourteen other volunteers had begun to dig a tunnel that was supposed to come out behind the Bolivian positions in an opening which, at a given moment, would begin to erupt like the crater of a volcano.

The eighty yards of wide, underground perforation were covered in eighteen days. And the volcano began to erupt a solid lava of machine-gun slugs, grenades, projectiles of all calibers, until the enemy positions were razed.

He remembered the blue, moonless night, the strange silence that had preceded the massacre, and the night that followed, when everything was over—two identical, sepulchral, palpitating silences. In between the two, only the position of the stars indicated the transition of a brief sequence. Everything was the same—except for the remnants of that fearful carnage that, in sum, had added a barely perceptible new detail to the design of the nocturnal landscape.

He remembered, a second before the attack, his vision of the enemy, submerged in the tranquil slumber from which they would not awake. He recalled having chosen his victims, covering them with the still silent swing of his machine gun. Above all, he remembered one of them: a soldier who writhed in the whirlwind of a nightmare. Perhaps in that moment he was dreaming of a tunnel identical with the one from which extermination was approaching. In a sufficiently extensive and flexible thought, such distinctions lack all real importance. The circumstance that one was the exterminator and the other the imminent victim was insignificant. But in that moment he had not yet realized that.

He only remembered that he had emptied his machine gun completely. He recalled that when the automatic weapon finally heated and jammed, he had abandoned it and had gone on throwing hand grenades until both arms grew numb. Strangest of all, while these things were happening he was plagued by memories of other things, real and imagined, that apparently had no relationship to each other and which increased his sensation of floating in a dream. He thought, for example, of his mother's crimson cape (real); of the immense bronze *panambí* at the tomb of the poet, Ortiz Guerrero (imagined); of his sister María Isabel, who had recently become a teacher (real). These incoherent blinkings of his imagination lasted all the while; he remembered returning with them, splashing through a swamp of viscid blood.

That tunnel of the Chaco and this tunnel, which he personally had suggested be dug in the prison floor, which he personally had begun to dig, and which had served him only as a deadly trap: this tunnel and that were the same tunnel—a single, straight, black perforation with an entrance but no exit; a straight, black perforation that, despite its straightness, had surrounded him from the time he was born like a subterranean, irrevocable, fatal circle; a tunnel that for him was forty years old now, but really much older, immortal in fact. That blue night in the Chaco, peopled with explosions and corpses, had falsely promised an exit. But it had only been a dream—less than a dream, the fantastic ornament of a futuristic reverie amid the smoke of battle.

With his last breath Perucho Rodi began once again to dream, except that now the faraway dream was real. And now he really devised the blind opening, the perfect circle of the exit. He dreamed—remembered—that he again climbed from that erupting crater into the blue, metallic, clamorous night. Again he felt the burning, convulsive machine gun in his hands. Again he fired burst after burst and hurled grenade after grenade. He saw the face of each one of his victims—eighty-nine in all. He recognized them in a sudden flash, and trembled: those eighty-nine living and terrible faces of his victims were—and would continue to be in the swift light of an infinite photoflash—the faces of his companions in prison. Included were those of the seventeen dead, to which one more had been added. He dreamed among those dead, dreamed that he was dreaming of a tunnel. He saw himself twisting in a nightmare; dreaming that he was digging, fighting, killing. He remembered clearly the enemy soldier he had machine-gunned while the other twisted in a nightmare. He dreamed that the enemy soldier—looking so much like himself as to be his twin brother—now with a machine gun . . . killed . . . him. Perucho Rodi's dream remained interred in that fissure like a black diamond.

The frustrated escape was discovered, as was the entrance mouth in the floor of the cell. This fact inspired the prison guards.

On the following night, the prisoners of Cell No. 4—except for escapee Perucho Rodi—found their door left inexplicably unlocked. Probing with their eyes the sinister fastnesses of the courtyard, they discovered the passages and corridors deserted. The rear door, opening onto a closed alley, hung ajar. The prisoners pushed it wide open and stepped outside. The crossfire of machine guns, spitting into the night air from dark embrasures in the walls of the alley, caught them and beat them to the cobbled paving.

Next day the city was informed only that a number of prisoners had been liquidated the moment they attempted to escape through a tunnel. The communique could lie truthfully; there was irrefutable testimony: the tunnel. Newspaper reporters were invited to examine it and evinced satisfaction on seeing the tunnel entrance in the cell. This evidence annulled a few insignificant details: the nonexistent exit (which no one asked to see) and the still fresh bloodstains in the abandoned alley.

A little later the opening was filled with stones and Cell No. 4 once again was locked.

Nivaria Tejera

The following poem is taken from one of the poet's two published volumes of verse, which reveal the influences of Rilke, Vallejo and Milosz, among others. Born in Cienfuegos (1930), Tejera spent the years of early childhood in the Canary Islands.

Fragments from *La gruta*

A butterfly has fallen here, nevertheless, in the hand, in the
    shade,
in the typical astonishment of the hours, in the doubling of
    the body,
and I no longer know what to do with this mute flight,
with this peace about to be resolved,
like one who goes seeking the terminus of water
and even in the depth encounters its bland movement.
With all this interminable tremor of something falling,
bones, or a smile, or faith.
And there is not a single sound to catch hold of,
the throat silent and the night and the world silent.
One sometimes knows not what to do with so much hope
    surprising him,
and he repeats: I am going to pay attention to things,
to children at play
or to the high balustrade;
one is entertained by containing an event
and suffers at seeing clearly, at being clearly something
    under his forehead;
he imagines the manner in which life is approaching
and even arrives completely.
A butterfly has fallen.
I must think that I walk beneath its dust.

Today something from infancy asks of us a tender mode,
a bird we have lived,

a silent profile that we have left behind
in any unpremeditated station;
a blush that gave us the wonder of those who do not smile,
or something that sounded beautiful because no longer used
and that we lost by matching ourselves to the days;
all that which can be lost because it is not ours
and which falls easily like a tear,
in the same way that life separates itself from us.
Then it must be understood: life goes on outside, but I am
    here;
it is important that birds greet each other
warbling the obscure gesture from inside of living,
from behind living.

Fragmentos del libro: La gruta

Se ha caído una mariposa aquí todavía, en la mano, en la
    sombra,
en el típico asombro de las horas, en el doblar del cuerpo,
y ya no sé que hacer con este vuelo mudo,
con esta paz por desatar,
como quien va buscando el final del agua
y aún en el fondo encuentra su movimiento blando.
Con todo ese temblor inacabable de que algo está cayendo,
los huesos, o la risa, o la fé.
Y no hay ningún ruido por donde detenerse,
la garganta en silencio y la noche y el mundo en silencio.
Uno no sabe a veces qué hacer con tanta esperanza que lo
    sorprende,
y se repite: voy a fijarme en las cosas,
en los niños que juegan
o en la baranda que quedó tan alta;
se entretiene conteniendo un suceso
y sufre de ver claro, de ser claramente algo bajo la frente,
imagina de la manera que la vida se va aproximando
y hasta llega del todo.

Se ha caído una mariposa.
He de pensar que ando debajo de su polvo.

Hoy algo de la infancia nos pide un grado tierno,
un pájaro vivido,
un perfil silencioso que perdimos atrás
en cualquier estación desprevenida;
un rubor que nos daba la extrañeza de los que no sonríen,
o algo que sonó hermoso porque ya no se usa
y que perdimos por igualarnos a los días;
todo eso que se puede perder porque no es de nosotros
y se cae fácil como una lágrima,
de la misma manera que la vida se nos va separando.
Entonces habrá que comprender: la vida sigue afuera pero
        yo estoy aquí,
es importante que los pajaros saluden
soplando el ademán oscuro hacia dentro de vivir,
hacia detrás de vivir.

ALBERTO RUBIO

A native of Chile, Rubio was born in the capital city of Santiago in 1928. He spent the year 1948-1949 in Spain as the holder of a Spanish government scholarship, and has published one book of poetry.

Portrait of a Little Girl

My heart feels slanted before this little girl.
Slanted are her eyes, slanted her eyebrows,
and her small forehead is a slanted square,
and, sharp, her chin tilts slantingly.

And she wears a slanted green, the green of her eyes,
in two slanted wings of slanted butterfly.
When the wind rises, her dress responds,
slanting the squarely green air.

Her golden cheekbones sharpen her face,
tilting it in hexagon of tilted sadness.
My heart feels slanted before this little girl,
tilts gilding itself, and green, feels wings.

Retrato de una niña

Mi corazón se siente oblicuo ante esta niña.
Oblicuos son sus ojos, oblicuas son sus cejas,
y su frente pequeña es un cuadrado oblicuo,
y aguda su barbilla, se ladea oblicuándose.

Y viste un verde oblicuo, el verde de los ojos,
en dos alas oblicuas de mariposa oblicua.
Cuando levanta el viento, su vestido se alza
oblicuando los aires cuadradamente verdes.

Los pómulos dorados le agudizan la cara,
ladeándola en exágono de ladeada tristeza.
Mi corazón se siente oblicuo ante esta niña,
se ladea dorándose, y verde, siente alas.

H. A. Murena

The author of two volumes of poetry, a volume of essays and a
play, Murena was born in 1919 in the Patagonian seaport of
Puerto Madryn, on Argentina's Atlantic coast. The death of
Edgar Allan Poe, which Murena here takes as his theme, occurred in Baltimore in 1849, on the eve of his second marriage.

Death of Edgar Allan Poe

It is well, he said. I no longer complain.
I had already imagined this horror as well:
the hostile city of Baltimore; the eternal,
frozen mist of autumn dawn
in the docks, all elfs missing;
and becoming the refuse that brusque hands
could drag off in a cart to the hospital;
and seeing myself thus.
Because I was yet an adolescent I recall,
the night when I wrote my first verse,
when I heard the whisper, the diminutive worm
of corruption initiating its march
in this Danish youth, the very minute
in which the valiant prince had already
been crowned for death, and then
I understood the deepest sense in which that prince was I.
They did not forgive my conjuring, my visions.
They would speak of gold and of cattle, of progress
and of sad machines, and I showed them
the vortex over which all trembles,
I wished to save them by one day bursting forth with
the poetry that through millenniums has slept
interred in the blood of men.
Unarmed gentleman of the real battle,
I went through cities with my staff; hated,

earing the inextinguishable race of earth
harpening without pause in its caves
he dagger prepared for me.
And, although I could have been a Byron,
lthough, perhaps for an instant could have spoken
o Shakespeare on equal terms, I reaped no more
han the hypnotic roses of crimes
nd terror, and in this phantasmal America,
ewitched from one end to the other,
die obscurely, defeated and ignored.
Now I feel only a heaviness of countenance,
he stupor of one abruptly
wrenched from vast and profound dreams.
t is well. I no longer complain.

Muerte de Edgar Allan Poe

stá bien—dijo—. Ya no me quejo.
También este horror había imaginado:
a hostil ciudad de Baltimore, la bruma
terna y helada del amanecer de otoño
n los muelles, todo elfo ausente,
ser el desperdicio que bruscas manos
udieron arrastrar en un carro al hospital,
así verme.
orque era un adolescente aún, recuerdo,
a noche en que escribía mi primer verso,
uando oí el susurro, el diminuto gusano
e la podredumbre iniciando su marcha
n esta joven Dinamarca, el minuto mismo
n que el valiente príncipe por la muerte
abía sido ya coronado, y entonces
omprendí en lo hondo que ese príncipe
ra yo.
No me perdonaron mis magias, mis visiones.
llos hablaban de oro y de ganados, de progresos
de tristes mecanismos, y yo les mostraba

el vórtice sobre el que todo tiembla,
quería salvarlos haciendo que un día estallara
la poesía que desde milenios duerme
sepulta en la sangre de los hombres.
Desarmado señor de la batalla verdadera,
yo iba por las ciudades, con mi tirso, odiado,
oyendo a la raza inextinguible del mundo
afilar sin pausa en sus cuevas
el puñal para mí preparado.
Y aunque hubiera podido ser un Byron,
aunque acaso por un instante hubiera hablado
con Shakespeare como un igual, no coseché
más que las hipnóticas rosas de los crímenes
y el pavor, y en esta América fantasmal,
hechizada del uno al otro extremo,
muero oscuro, vencido e ignorado.
Ahora solo siento una pesadez en el rostro,
el estupor de aquel a quien abruptamente
han arrancado de vastos y profundos sueños.
Está bien. Ya no me quejo.

JUAN JOSE ARREOLA

A recipient of grants from both the French government and the Rockefeller Foundation, Arreola has published two collections of short stories. He was born in Zapotlan, Mexico, in 1918. In the following tale, which reveals an intermingling of Kafkian and purist tendencies, satire is the weapon selected for the author's dissection of humanity.

The Prodigious Milligram

An ant often reprimanded for the lightness of her burdens and for her frequent distractions discovered one morning, on detouring again from the highway, a prodigious milligram—an even one-thousandth of a gram. Without stopping to ponder the consequences of the discovery, she seized the milligram and placed it on her back. It was, she realized joyously, exactly the right load for her. The ideal weight of the object lent her body strange energy, as wings help a bird to soar. Actually, one of the causes of premature death among ants is their ambitious lack of consideration for their own frailties. After delivering a grain of corn to the granary, the ant that has carried it more than half a mile retains scarcely enough strength to drag her own body to the cemetery.

The ant that made the discovery was unaware of her luck, but her steps betrayed the anxious rapidity of one who flees with a treasure. A vague but healthy feeling of vindication began to replenish her spirits. After a long, roundabout detour, made in holiday mood, she joined a string of companions returning, as evening fell, with the load required for that day: small fragments of lettuce leaf carefully cut during the day's work. The ants' highway formed a slender and blurred battlement of tiny foliage. It was impossible to deceive anybody: the milligram was

99

terribly out of place in the middle of that perfect uniformity.

In the anthill the situation was even worse. The gate guards and inspectors in all the galleries objected, each one more strenuously, to the strange burden. The words "milligram" and "prodigious" sounded here and there on the lips of certain knowledgeable ones. The chief inspectress, seated solemnly at an imposing table, was the first to link the words, saying ironically to the confused ant: "Probably you have brought us a prodigious milligram. I congratulate you with all my heart, but my duty is to inform the police."

Public functionaries are the persons least adept at resolving questions of prodigies and of milligrams. Confronted with a case unforeseen by the penal code, they proceeded in accordance with everyday ordinances, seizing the milligram and the ant as well. As the ant's previous record was of the worst possible sort, it was judged that the proper legal procedure should be a criminal action. The qualified authorities took charge of the affair.

The habitual slowness of judicial proceedings clashed with the anxiety of the ant, whose strange conduct prejudiced even her own attorneys. Obeying the dictates of deeply rooted convictions, she answered arrogantly all questions put to her. She spread the rumor that grave injustices were being done to her, and announced that very soon her enemies would be forced to recognize the importance of her discovery. Such absurdities brought down on her nearly all available sanctions. At the height of her pride, she said that she sincerely regretted forming part of so imbecile an anthill. On hearing these words, the prosecuting attorney, in a stentorian voice, demanded the death sentence.

In this situation the ant's salvation was won by the testimony of a celebrated alienist, who established her mental unbalance.

At night, instead of sleeping, the prisoner would commence turning her milligram over and over; she would polish it carefully, and would spend long hours in a sort of contemplative ecstasy. During the day she carried it on her shoulders from one side of the narrow, dark cell to the other. She approached the end of her life a victim of terrible agitation—so much so that the prison doctor asked, on three occasions, that her cell be changed. Each succeeding cell was larger, but the ant's agitation increased with the space available. She paid not the slightest attention to all the curious who came in increasing numbers to watch the spectacle of her disorderly death pangs· She stopped eating almost entirely; she refused to receive newspapermen, and she maintained an absolute silence.

Higher authorities finally decided to transfer the crazed ant to a sanitarium. But official decisions always suffer from slowness.

One day, on awakening, the jailer found the cell quiet and filled with a strange splendor. The prodigious milligram glittered on the floor like a diamond ablaze with its own light. Near it lay the heroic ant, feet in the air, wasted and transparent.

The news of her death and the prodigious virtues of the milligram swept like a flood through all the galleries. Caravans of visitors examined the cell, improvised into a lighted chapel. Ants flung themselves on the floor in their despair. From their eyes, dazzled by the vision of the milligram, flowed tears in such abundance that funeral arrangements were complicated by a drainage problem. Lacking adequate floral offerings, the shaken ants raided the storehouses to cover the corpse of the victim with pyramids of food.

The anthill lived through indescribable days, a mixture of admiration, pride and sorrow. They organized sumptuous obsequies topped off with balls and banquets. Rapidly they commenced building a sanctuary for the milligram, and the misunderstood, murdered ant won the honor of a mausoleum. The authorities were deposed and accused of treason.

Somewhat later, despite great difficulties, a council of elders began to function, putting an end to the prolonged period of orgiastic honors. Life returned to its normal course thanks to numerous executions. The wisest elders then guided the torrent of devout admiration which the milligram had awakened into an increasingly strict form of official religion. Guardians and priests were appointed. A circle of great buildings sprouted around the sanctuary, and an extensive bureaucracy began to occupy them in accordance with rigorous hierarchy. The economic capacity of the flourishing anthill was seriously compromised.

Worst of all, disorder, driven from the surface, enjoyed a disturbing, subterranean life. Apparently the anthill lived tranquilly and compactly, devoted to labor and worship, in spite of the great number of functionaries who spent their lives discharging less and less important tasks. It is impossible to say which ant harbored the first pernicious thoughts in his mind. Perhaps there were many who began thinking at the same time and fell into temptation.

In any case, those involved were ambitious, blinded ants who meditated blasphemously on the humble state of the discoverer. They dimly saw the possibility that all the homage paid the deceased might be bestowed on them in this life. They began to adopt suspicious attitudes. Straying and melancholy, they wandered purposely from the road and returned to the anthill with empty hands. They answered the inspectors with poorly disguised arrogance; frequently, they would pass themselves off as sick and would promise a sensational discovery in the near future. The authorities themselves could not dismiss the idea that one of those lunatics might very well arrive with a prodigy on his weak shoulders.

The ants who were involved worked secretly. Had a general interrogation been possible, the authorities would have been forced to conclude that 50 per cent of the ants, instead of worrying about petty grains and fragile leaves, had their eyes fixed on the incorruptible substance of the milligram.

One day the inevitable occurred. As if they had agreed beforehand, six common ants—apparently of the most ordinary sort—arrived at the anthill, each with a strange object which was passed off, amid general anticipation, as a prodigious milligram. Naturally, they did not obtain the honors they had hoped for, but they were excused that

same day from all further service and were granted
pensions.

It was impossible to say anything concrete about the
six milligrams. Memory of their previous imprudence dis-
suaded the authorities from all judicial action. The elders
washed their hands of the matter in council and granted
the public ample liberty of opinion. In the showcases of a
modest enclosure the milligrams in question were offered
to public view, and all the ants expressed their opinion in
accordance with their honest knowledge and understanding.

This weakness on the part of the authorities plus the
culpable silence of the critics precipitated the ruin of the
anthill. From then on, any ant, worn out by work or
tempted by laziness, could reduce his ambitions of glory to
the limits of a lifelong pension, free from servile obligations.
And the anthill began to fill with false milligrams.

In vain certain old and wise ants recommended pre-
cautionary measures, such as the use of scales and the
minute comparison of each new milligram with the original
model. Nobody paid attention to them. Their proposals,
which were not even discussed in assembly, came to an
end with the declarations of a scrawny and discolored ant
who openly and loudly proclaimed his personal opinions.
According to this nihilist, the famous, original milligram,
however prodigious it might be, should not set a precedent
of quality. Prodigiousness should not be required as a
necessary condition of the newly discovered milligrams.

The small amount of contention which remained among
the ants disappeared with such ill-advised words. From then
on the authorities were incapable of limiting or appraising
the objects which the anthill might receive daily under the
category of milligrams. All right of veto was denied them,
and they could not even insure that each ant fulfilled his
obligations. All wanted to free themselves from servitude
by hunting milligrams.

The storehouses for these articles came to occupy two-
thirds of the anthill—not counting private collections,
some of them famed for the value of their pieces. As far
as ordinary milligrams were concerned, their value dropped

so that in the days of greatest affluence they could be obtained in exchange for any trifle. It must not be denied that from time to time certain valuable specimens reached the anthill. But they had the same fate as the worst rubbish. Legions of enthusiasts dedicated themselves to praising milligrams of the most dubious quality, thus fomenting a general demoralization.

In their desperation, many ants brought in the worst trash and filth. Entire galleries were closed for reasons of health. The example of one extravagant ant would find thousands of imitators the following day. At the cost of great effort, and employing all their reserves of common sense, the elders of the council continued calling themselves authorities and made vague attempts to govern.

Bureaucrats and members of the faith, not content with their leisurely situations, abandoned church and office to hurl themselves into the search for milligrams in an effort to increase their emoluments and honors. The police force practically ceased to exist; riots and revolutions were daily experiences. Bands of professional thugs lurked in the neighborhood of the anthill to despoil the fortunate ones who returned with valuable milligrams. Resentful collectors denounced their rivals and promoted lengthy trials, seeking the vengeance of public disgrace and expropriation. Disputes within the galleries degenerated easily into brawls, and these into murders. The mortality rate reached a frightful figure. Births decreased in an alarming manner, and the young, lacking adequate attention, died by hundreds.

The sanctuary guarding the true milligram became a no man's land. The ants, occupied in the discussions which the most scandalous finds aroused, no longer bothered to visit it. From time to time some residual devotee called the authorities' attention to its state of ruin and abandonment. The most that was accomplished was a bit of cleaning. A half-dozen irreverent street sweepers would apply a few broom strokes, while decrepit ancients delivered long discourses and covered the ant's tomb with deplorable offerings, largely composed of trash.

Buried beneath threatening clouds of disorder, the

prodigious milligram shone in its obscurity. A scandalous bit of news began to circulate to the effect that it had been stolen by sacrilegious hands; a poor copy replaced the authentic milligram, which now belonged to the collection of a criminal ant whose wealth had derived from traffic in milligrams. Such rumors were untrue, but nobody troubled himself or worried; nobody carried out an investigation to put them to rest. And the ancients of the council, growing daily weaker and more infirm, folded their arms in the face of imminent disaster.

Winter approached, and the threat of death halted the delirium of the improvident ants. In the face of the food crisis, the authorities decided to sell a large quantity of milligrams to a neighboring community of wealthy ants. All they succeeded in doing was to rid themselves of a few pieces of true worth for a handful of vegetables and grain. In exchange for the original milligram, they were offered enough food to tide them through the winter.

The bankrupt anthill clung to its milligram as to a life raft. After interminable conferences and discussions, when hunger finally had diminished the number of survivors, to the benefit of their rich neighbors, the latter opened the doors of their home to the owners of the prodigy. They contracted to feed them to the end of their days and to exempt them from all work. On the death of the last "outside" ant, the milligram would become the property of the purchasers.

Needless to say, the guests in the new anthill lost no time in spreading the germs of their contagious idolatry. Now, forgetting their traditionally practical and utilitarian habits, ants everywhere have given themselves over to a frenzied search for milligrams. They eat away from the anthill, and they store only light, glittering objects. Very soon, perhaps, they will disappear as a zoological species, and they will leave to us, preserved in two or three ineffective fables, merely the memory of their ancient virtues.

CINTIO VITIER

A Cuban, born in Key West, Florida, in 1921, Vitier has published one book of essays, a volume of poems and two anthologies of Cuban poetry.

Words of the Prodigal Son

I

The light has dimmed now, and the soul
takes possession of the exiled wind
that moves what I at last possess,
the barks of a far-off peace.

My time is now becalmed
where for a while I sweetly love,
and the old-time voice of a mother
spreads itself like bleached cloth.

The light is dim, after all, and the angel hears
my heart, still turbid and stony
from its lost vanity, empty
in the color of the year.

Because man, who must die, toils,
and in dark garments becomes enraptured,
but at times also trembles and sings,
like a worker returning.

II

I rejoice to see the carpenter
who arrives with his fine tools
and the grave measure of his countenance.
He is, besides, a man who has suffered.
The same I say of the mechanic

and of the rough and patient bricklayers.
It is consoling, in some way,
to watch those who know how
to live in the sacred company
of matter and the proportions
that serve to erect buildings.
Those who have clear eyes,
precise muscles, hands that know
the grain and the texture and the
rebellious or docile tendencies of things.
Those who, in reality, expect
to become white dust, children of penury,
and in the hereafter, serenely, nothing.
These men possess a special silence.
In the immense world
of prophets and constellations
they see only a humble task before them,
so small or so pure
that at times it is unimaginable.
And when they are absorbed, working,
in the most profound instant of their craft,
I have seen that a soft light
gently touches them, distends their wrinkles,
and delicately separates them from death.

III

The sentinel, muffled
against nocturnal vapors, hears a silence
like a sigh, and then sound
the flourishes, precursors of another dark yesterday.
Ah, the hoarse voices of command! Soon
bodies will clash, eyes
attentive, sparkling, or veiled
souls contemplating their destiny
like a far-distant battle.
But here someone
(in some remote place,
perhaps surrounded by beggars and thieves,

in the tavern, or alone,
gazing at the rooftops of the villa)
chooses that moment, that vacuum
in which everything is suspended before dawn,
to raise in it a thin line,
only a line, a thread
like the virginal border of a veil,
wounding, almost, because so sweet;
and when all are sleeping on earth,
their bones disjointed by nothingness,
their names already erased
from even the most humble hands and mouths,
we hear clearly
that violin above the emptiness,
that sorrow so pure, that
crystalline smile that issues from a small canvas,
that verse, Lord—the voice
that rises from the dawn
where all is suspended before itself,
and sings the joy of men.

IV

Succession cannot break the line
—while it endures, eternal—of the Virgin of Pasellino,
thin as the air that circulates in the words
of light, water or spirit, when within,
in this clairvoyant interior, is illumined her velatura
to make of the blind instant a mansion where crystalline
        reasons
hold dialogue. But one day that gilt
that was the attentive palm of gray, those eyes
that were the ardent transfiguration of days, in Florence
or here, where I feel now that I am distant as a star,
that line which took from the sea its timid aureole,
will be a cold twilight wandering among the names
that dawn, splendid and fine, on the lips of angels.

V

And when we awaken, with the silent
cry of yearning, the darkness
vibrates like a door
that someone has just slammed violently.
Who flees then through lonely fields,
or who glances gently, with the moon's eye
spilled upon a chair, through certain books?
Or who tells us: come, this is the empty
stage of the theater; in your dreams
you will find what you were seeking?
Or who begins to syllabize sacred names
that soon are images chanting
between forgetfulness and memory, and then birds
quarreling in the dawn?
                    From all this
has my interrogative life been woven, and each thing
—each filament of time—surprises me
like a blind man on the immense doorstep,
wistful, with hands outstretched.

VI

And what am I
other than the site of change, the place
where cold and heat happen,
my age composed of days,
of slownesses and brevities,
of glorious surprises and unspeakable tediums,
of hopes and desperations,
all weaving the anguished hour
of that twilight in which I am
watching myself enter into me definitively,
like night into the desert?
But the site of change, which is I,
is it within or outside this dream?
And it, in itself, does it not change?

Is it fixed like an idea, separated
from change like the idea of a discourse,
like the truth which may be pronounced
by Socrates or by
a stone or a cedar? And, nevertheless,
I sometimes awaken at midnight, or midst the smoke,
pleasing to the soul, from the friendly conversation,
and I feel the supplicating glance,
infinite, gentle, imploring,
of what could be called my truth, full of change,
of indecisive lights and savage forgetting,
bathed in tears, siren
of chance or destiny, beyond
the melancholy grasp of my hands.

VII

Vagabond fable of innocence,
castle that falls apart and rolls,
silent clangor, vacant vision,
eye destroyed by solitudes,
hand of immense and gentle decisions,
mouth of ephemeral cantatas,
empty guffaw of the actor,
mythological groups, winged bull,
incessant apocalypses, people,
serene storehouses of nothingness,
mutilations of the athlete, leaps,
friezes, advertisements, fables,
cornucopias, cupolas, desires,
exclusive toyshop of chance,
sphinx with destroyed smile,
mechanic of the dream, cemetery,
Homeric battle, meditation of Caesar,
noon in Italian convents,
face of Medicis, burning stake of heresy,
sermon of snow, flying market place,
orgy of crystalline volutes,
dead-white togas, veils of the Virgin,

granaries, arms, cathedrals,
galleons breaking apart in the light,
innocent islands, untouched bays,
terror, sacrifice, sensuality,
prayer, parchment, dream,
clamorous multitude gesticulating,
garden of mutilated statues,
empire destroyed in the memory,
enigmatic, sobbing news,
vulgar bazaar, dark merry-go-round,
nightfall in the lonely bed,
empty succession, unhappy whiteness,
slow, inaudible explosions,
imaginary time in space,
broken altar, substance of history, clouds.

VIII

> And when he had spent all, there
> arose a great famine in that land;
> and he began to be in want.
> LUKE 15:14

When I came to the end
of the street nothing had changed.
Yes, nothing had changed. The change
was an emptiness shining in the windows and clouds.
It was the same place that had always been another
—twilight knows how to change an emptiness—
and I walked by the same backdrop,
perhaps watched by an enthusiastic public
who in moments of forgetting walk the street.
Perhaps it would have been better not to come
and see that nothing had changed,
that here were the familiar places, as strange
as ever, that always had been that way,
although something was missing, which I could not remem-
    ber,
which always had been missing.

I grew weak then in a dreadful way,
I lost substance or someone
I could not name stole it from me;
I was like a child that suddenly
has begun to forget all notion of time
and no longer sustains the idea of his being, and hears
a vague clangor spilling coldness
in the center of his heart.
It was an epoch of changes and twilights.
I came undone then, but the air
I remembered was missing; like a dream
of unsuspected whiteness it began to awaken me;
since everything was so gentle,
so full of nothingness, so much the same and so different,
and that which was lacking in everything was so pure,
I knew my home, or whatever the place
that impelled me, could not be very far.

Palabras del hijo prodigo

I

La luz es poca ya, y el alma
se apodera del viento desterrado
que mueve lo que al fin poseo,
las naves de una paz lejana.

En calma está mi tiempo
donde a ratos dulcemente amo,
y la voz antigua de una madre
se extiende como tela de blancura.

La luz es poca al fin, y el ángel oye
mi corazón aún turbio y pedregoso
de su perdida vanidad, vacío
en el color del año.

Porque el hombre que ha de morir trabaja
y en hábitos oscuros se extasía,

pero a veces también tiembla y canta,
como un trabajador que vuelve.

II

Me alegra ver al carpintero
que llega con sus finas herramientas
y la grave mesura de su rostro.
Es, además, un hombre que ha sufrido.
Lo mismo digo del mecánico
y de los rudos y pacientes albañiles.
Consuela, de algún modo,
mirar a los que saben
vivir en la sagrada compañía
de la materia y de las proporciones,
que sirven para hacer los edificios.
A los que tienen ojos claros,
músculos precisos, manos que conocen
el grano y la textura y la tendencia
rebelde o dócil de las cosas.
A los que en realidad esperan
ser polvo blanco, hijos de penuria,
y más allá, serenamente, nada.
Estos hombres poseen un especial silencio.
En el inmenso mundo
de los profetas y las constelaciones,
sólo ven ante sí una tarea humilde,
tan pequeña o tan pura
que a veces no es posible imaginarla.
Y cuando están absortos trabajando,
en el instante más profundo de su oficio,
yo he visto que una lumbre suave,
suavísima los toca y distiende sus arrugas,
y delicadamente los separa de la muerte.

III

El centinela, enmascarado
de vapores nocturnos, oye un silencio

como un suspiro, y luego suenan
las dianas precursoras de otro ayer oscuro.
Ah, las roncas voces de mando! Pronto
van a chocar los cuerpos, los ojos
atentos, chispeantes, o velados,
las almas contemplando su destino
como una batalla lejanísima.

Pero he aquí que alguien
(en algún remoto sitio,
tal vez rodeado de mendigos y ladrones,
en la taberna, o solo,
mirando los techos de la villa),
escoge ese minuto, ese vacío
en que todo está suspenso ante la aurora,
para alzar en él una delgada línea,
sólo una línea, un hilo
como el borde virginal de un velo,
hiriente casi de tan dulce;
y cuando todos duermen en la tierra
desunidos sus huesos por la nada,
borrados ya sus nombres
hasta de las manos y las bocas más humildes,
sentimos claramente
aquel violín sobre el vacío,
aquel dolor tan puro, aquella
sonrisa cristalina que sale de un pequeño lienzo,
aquel verso, Señor —aquella voz
que se levanta de la aurora
en que todo está suspenso ante sí mismo,
y canta la alegría de los hombres.

IV

No puede la sucesión romper la línea
—mientras dura, eterna—de la virgen de Pesellino,
delgada como el aire que circula en las palabras
de la luz, el agua o el espíritu, cuando por dentro,
en ese interior vidente, se ilumina su veladura
para hacer del ciego instante una mansión donde dialogan

cristalinas razones. Pero un día, aquel dorado
que era del gris la palma atenta, aquellos ojos
que eran la transfiguración ardiente de los días, en Florencia
o aquí, donde ahora siento que soy distante como un astro,
aquella línea que sacaba del mar su tímida aureola,
será un frío crepúsculo vagando entre los nombres
que amanecen, espléndidos y finos, en los labios de los
  ángeles.

V

Y cuando despertamos, con el grito
silencioso del anhelo, está vibrando
la oscuridad como una puerta
que alguien acabara de cerrar vehementemente.
¿Quién huye entonces por los campos solitarios,
o quién mira dulce, con el ojo de la luna
derramada en una silla, en unos libros?
¿O quién nos dice: ven, esto es la escena
vacía del teatro, es en tus sueños
donde vas a encontrar lo que buscabas?
¿O quién empieza a silabear sagrados nombres
que luego son imágenes cantando
entre el olvido y la memoria, y luego pájaros
riñendo en el albor?
    De todo esto
se ha tejido mi vida interrogante, y cada cosa
—cada brizna de tiempo—me sorprende
como un ciego en el inmenso umbral,
ansioso, con las manos extendidas.

VI

¿Y qué soy yo
sino el sitio del cambio, el lugar
donde acontece el frío y el calor,
la edad hecha de días,
de lentitudes y fugacidades,
de sorpresas gloriosas e indecibles hastíos,

de esperanzas y desesperanzas,
todo tejiendo la angustiosa hora
de ese crepúsculo en que estoy
mirándome entrar en mí, definitivamente,
como la noche en el desierto?
Pero el sitio del cambio, que soy yo,
¿está dentro o está fuera de este sueño?
Y él mismo, en sí, ¿no cambia?
¿Está fijo como una idea, separado
del cambio como la idea del discurso,
como la verdad que puede ser pronunciada
por Sócrates o por
una piedra o un cedro? Y, sin embargo,
a veces despierto a medianoche, o entre el humo,
grato al alma, de la amistosa conversación,
y siento la mirada suplicante,
infinita, dulce, suplicante,
de lo que se dice mi verdad, llena de cambio,
de luces indecisas y de salvaje olvido,
bañada en lágrimas, sirena
del azar o del destino, más allá
del melancólico alcance de mis manos.

VII

Bestiario errante de candor,
castillo que se desune y rueda,
estruendo silencioso, visión nula,
ojo deshecho de las soledades,
mano de inmensas y dulces decisiones,
boca de efímeras cantatas,
carcajada hueca del actor,
mitológicas grupas, toro alado,
apocalipsis incesantes, pueblos,
serenos almacenes de la nada,
mutilaciones del atleta, salto,
frisos, anuncios, fábulas,
cornucopias, cúpulas, deseos,
juguetería pura del azar,

esfinge de sonrisa destrozada,
mecánica del sueño, camposanto,
batalla homérica, meditación de César,
mediodía en conventos italianos,
rostro de Médicis, hoguera del hereje,
sermón de nieve, ágora volando,
orgía de volutas cristalinas,
togas blanquísimas, velos de la Virgen,
graneros, armas, catedrales,
galeones rompiéndose en la luz,
islas sencillas, bahías intocadas,
el terror, el sacrificio, la lujuria,
la plegaria, el pergamino, el sueño,
estentórea multitud gesticulando,
jardín de estatuas injuriadas,
imperio destruído en la memoria,
enigmáticas noticias sollozando,
feria vulgar, oscuro tiovivo,
la llegada de noche al lecho solo,
vacía sucesión, blancor infausto,
inaudibles y lentas explosiones,
imaginario tiempo en el espacio,
roto altar, sustancia de la historia, nubes.

VIII

Después que lo gastó todo, sobre-
vino una grande hambre en aquel país,
y comenzó a padecer necesidad.

S. LUCAS, 15:14

Cuando llegué al final
de la calle, nada había cambiado.
Sí, nada había cambiado. El cambio
era la nada brillando en las ventanas y las nubes.
Era el mismo lugar que siempre había sido otro,
el crepúsculo sabe cambiar la nada,
y yo paseaba por las bambalinas de lo mismo
tal vez mirado por un ardiente público

que en sus ratos de olvido pasea por la calle.
Acaso hubiera sido mejor no haber venido
para ver que nada había cambiado,
que allí estaban los sitios familiares, tan extraños
como siempre, que siempre había sido así,
aunque faltaba algo, lo que no podía recordar,
lo que siempre había faltado.
Me debilitaba entonces en una forma horrenda,
perdía sustancia o alguien
a quien no podía nombrar me la robaba,
era como una criatura que de pronto
ha empezado a olvidar toda noción del tiempo
y no sostiene ya la idea de su ser, y escucha
un vago estruendo derramando frialdades
en el centro de su corazón.
Era una época de cambios y crepúsculos.
Me deshacía entonces, pero el aire
que ahora notaba ausente, como un sueño
de inesperada blancura empezaba a despertarme,
porque todo era tan dulce,
tan lleno de su nada, tan igual y tan distinto,
y lo que a todo le faltaba era tan puro,
que mi casa, o lo que fuera
el lugar que me impulsaba, no podía estar muy lejos.

Rosario Castellanos

Among the published works of this Mexican-born poet are *Los misterios gozosas* and *Al pie de la letra*. In 1950, at the age of twenty-five, she completed her studies in philosophy at the University of Mexico and was awarded a Spanish government scholarship for a postgraduate course in Madrid. The literary influences of Gabriela Mistral and of indigenous Aztec Indian poetry have played an important role in her work.

The Empty House

I remember a house I have left.
Now it is empty.
The curtains stir with the wind,
boards lash obstinately
against old walls.
In the garden, where grass begins
to overflow its empire,
in drawing rooms with covered furniture,
in deserted mirrors
solitude walks, glides, shod
in silent and soft velvet.

Here where its foot impresses a print,
in this hollow, smothered corridor
a young girl grew, here sprouted
her body of slender, mournful cypress.
(Down her back stretched two braids
like twin guardian angels.
Her hands never did anything
more than to close windows.)

Gray adolescence with vocation of shadow,
with destiny of death:
the stairway sleeps; the house
which knew not how to hold you, crumbles.

119

La casa vacia

Yo recuerdo una casa que he dejado.
Ahora está vacía.
Las cortinas se mecen con el viento,
golpean las maderas tercamente
contra los muros viejos.
En el jardin, donde la hierba empieza
a derramar su imperio,
en las salas de muebles enfundados,
en espejos desiertos
camina, se desliza la soledad calzada
de silencioso y blando terciopelo.

Aquí donde su pie marca la huella,
en este corredor profundo y apagado
crecía una muchacha, levantaba
su cuerpo de ciprés esbelto y triste.
(A su espalda crecían sus dos trenzas
igual que dos gemelos ángeles de la guarda.
Sus manos nunca hicieron otra cosa
más que cerrar ventanas.)

Adolescencia gris con vocación de sombra,
con destino de muerte:
las escaleras duermen, se derrumba
la casa que no supo detenerte.

Mario Benedetti

Among the published works of this prolific author and co-director of the literary review, *Numero*, are two volumes of poetry, two collections of essays, two volumes of short stories and a novel. He was born in the town of Paso de los Toros, Uruguay, in 1920.

Gloria's Saturday

Even before waking, I heard the rain falling. At first I thought it must be six-fifteen in the morning and I should be going to the office. But I had left my rubbers at my mother's house and would have to put newspaper in my other shoes, the everyday ones, because the damp cold, freezing my feet and ankles, drives me crazy. Then I thought it was Sunday and I could stay under the blankets for a while. The certainty of a holiday always gives me a childish pleasure: to know that I can dispose of my time as though I were free, as though I didn't have to run two blocks, four mornings out of six, to beat the clock on which I must register my arrival; to know that I can adopt a serious attitude and think of important things—life, death, football, war.

During the week I have no time. When I arrive at the office there are fifty or sixty matters waiting for me which I have to convert into accounting entries, stamp with the accounting seal and date, and initial in green ink. At twelve o'clock I have finished about half the work, and I run four blocks in order to ride on the bus platform. If I don't run those blocks, I have to hang onto the side of the bus and it makes me feel sick to pass so close to the streetcars. It isn't nausea, really, but fear, a horrible fear.

This doesn't mean that I think about death, only that it sickens me to imagine myself lying shattered and broken among two hundred preoccupied curiosity-seekers stretching and jostling to see me so they can tell everything, with gestures, over luncheon dessert—a family luncheon similar to the one I shall finish in twenty-five minutes, completely alone. Gloria goes to the store half an hour earlier and leaves everything ready for me in four pans on the stove over a slow fire, so I have nothing to do but wash my hands and swallow the soup, the macaroni, the tortilla and compote, glance at the newspaper, and rush out again to hunt for a bus. When I arrive back at the office at two, I set about the twenty or thirty operations that were left over. At about five, notebook in hand, I answer the punctual buzz of the vice-president, who dictates to me the customary half-dozen letters which I must deliver, translated into English or German, before seven o'clock.

Twice a week Gloria waits for me at the door. For amusement we go to a movie, where she cries copiously and I crush my hat or chew the program. The other days she goes to see her mother, and I take care of the accounting for two bakeries. Their owners—two Galicians and a Majorcan—earn a tidy sum manufacturing biscuits with rotten eggs, and earn even more from managing the most overcrowded tenements in the southern part of town. When I return home, Gloria is usually asleep. Or, when we return together, we eat dinner and go to bed immediately, weary as animals. Without even saying goodnight sometimes, we fall asleep with the light still on, because she wanted to read the crime reports and I, the sports page.

The commentaries await a Saturday like this one, the end of a Saturday nap. I get up at three-thirty to prepare tea and milk and bring it back to bed. She wakes up then, reviews the weekly routine, and mends my socks before getting up at quarter to five to hear the bolero hour. But this Saturday there would have been no commentaries, because last night after the movies I went too far in praising the leading lady. Without a moment's hesitation Gloria began to scratch me. Then, as I continued, she attacked with something much more insidious—the flattering description of a man who works in the store with her. It was unfair, naturally, because the actress was an image and this character, a flesh and blood idiot. Because of this nonsense, we went to bed without speaking and waited half and hour with the light off to see if the other would begin the business of reconciliation. It didn't matter to me if I were the first, like so many other times; but sleep came before the sham of anger ended, and the peacemaking was postponed for today, for the blank space after this nap.

That is why I felt pleased when I saw it was raining. The bad weather outside would automatically reinforce our intimacy, and neither of us would be so idiotic as to spend a rainy Saturday afternoon in haughty silence. In a two-room apartment solitude does not exist; everything is reduced to living face to face.

Gloria woke up with a groan, but I thought nothing of it. She always groans when she wakes up. But when she came wide awake, I looked at her face and saw that she was really sick. Suffering was patent in the circles under her eyes. I forgot then that we weren't speaking and asked her what was wrong. Something in her side hurt her. It hurt her badly, and she was afraid.

I told her I was going to call the registered nurse and she said, yes, to call her right away. She tried to smile, but her eyes were so sunken that I vacillated between staying with her or going to make the telephone call. Then I thought that if I didn't go, she would become more frightened, so I went downstairs and called the nurse.

The fellow who answered my call said the nurse wasn't at home. I don't know why it occurred to me he was lying, but I told him that wasn't true because I had already seen the nurse enter her house. Then he told me to wait a minute. After five minutes he returned to the phone and told me I was in luck because the nurse had just come in that very minute. I told him that was fine and made him take down the address, stressing the need for haste.

When I came back, Gloria's side hurt her much more. I didn't know what to do. I gave her a hot water bottle and afterwards an ice bag. Nothing quieted her, so I gave her an aspirin. At four the nurse hadn't come, and I was too nervous to encourage Gloria. I told her three or four funny stories, but when she smiled with a grimace I hated myself because I understood that she didn't want to discourage me. I had a glass of milk, nothing else, because I felt a lump in my stomach. At five-thirty the nurse finally showed up. She was an enormous female—her bulk filled the apartment. Emitting a couple of simulated giggles, she began to squeeze Gloria's side. She would sink her fingers in, then suddenly let go. Gloria would bite her lips and say, yes, it hurt there, and a little more there, and still more over there. It hurt more all the time.

The woman kept digging her fingers in and suddenly letting go. When she straightened up, her eyes were frightened too and she asked for alcohol to disinfect her hands. In the corridor she told me it was peritonitis and that it was necessary to operate immediately. I told her we had a health plan membership and she assured me that she would call the surgeon. I went down with her and called a taxi as well as Gloria's mother, then climbed the stairs because someone on the sixth floor had left the elevator door open. Gloria was all doubled up and, although her eyes were dry, I knew she was crying. I made her put on my overcoat and scarf and we started to leave.

Her mother arrived as we went out and said, "Poor thing" and "Wrap yourself up, for heaven's sake." Then Gloria seemed to understand that she had to be strong. In the taxi she made a few jokes about the obligatory vacation they would give her in the store, and that I wouldn't have socks for Monday, and—as her mother by this time was virtually a fountain—that what did she think this was, a soap opera? I knew that she was feeling worse and worse all the time, and she realized that I knew and squeezed against me.

When we arrived at the hospital, we left her in a small waiting room. After a while the surgeon came. He was a tall sort with a distracted, kindly look and wore an unbuttoned, dirty smock. Ordering us to leave, he closed the door. Gloria's mother sat on a low chair, crying more and more copiously. I looked out at the street; it wasn't raining now. I hadn't even the consolation of smoking. Even in my high school days I was the only one among thirty-eight who had never tried a cigarette. It was in high school that I met Gloria. She had black braids and couldn't pass geography. There were two ways to get to know her: teach her geography or learn it with her. The last was the most appropriate and, naturally, we both flunked.

Then the doctor came out and asked me if I were the brother or the husband. I told him the husband and he coughed asthmatically.

"It isn't peritonitis," he said. "The nurse is an ass."

"Oh."

"It is something else. Tomorrow we will know more."

Tomorrow. That means . . .

"We will know more, if she gets through the night. If we operate now, she's finished. It's quite serious, but if she gets past today I think she can be saved."

I thanked him—I don't know what I thanked him for —and he added, "It's against the rules, but you can stay with her tonight."

First, a nurse came by with my overcoat and scarf. Then Gloria came by on a stretcher, her eyes closed, unconscious.

At eight I was allowed to enter the single room where they had put Gloria. Beside the bed there were a chair and table. I sat straddling the chair and rested my elbows on the back. I felt a nervous pain in my eyelids as if my eyes were too wide open. I couldn't stop looking at her. The sheet was a continuation of the pallidness of her face. Her forehead was shiny, waxen. It was a delight to hear her breathe, even thus, with her eyes closed. I pretended that she had argued with me because I liked the film actress, and that I struck back at her because her fellow worker at the store was so agreeable. But deep inside I knew the truth. I felt as though I were in mid-air, as though this forced insomnia were an unfortunate reality that demanded of me this temporary tension, a tension that might terminate at any moment.

Once each eternity a clock struck far away. Only an hour had passed.

Once I got up, went out into the corridor and walked a few steps. Some fellow came up to me, biting a cigarette, and asked with a grimacing, radiant face, "Are you waiting too?"

I told him, yes, I was waiting too. Then I felt myself go weak, so went back to the room to straddle the chair. I began to count the tiles and to play superstitious games, setting traps for myself—estimating the number of tiles in a row and telling myself that if it were an uneven number, she would be saved. And it was uneven. Also she would be saved if the clock struck before I counted ten. And the clock struck when I reached five or six. Suddenly I found myself thinking, "If she gets through today . . ." and became panicky.

I had to make sure of the future, to imagine it at all costs, so that I could wrench Gloria away from this blossoming death. I started to think that on our annual vacation we would go to Floresta, that next Sunday—it was necessary to create a very near future—we would go to have dinner with my brother and his wife. We would laugh with them at my mother-in-law's fright. Gloria and I would have a child, two children, four children, and each time I would be waiting impatiently in the corridor.

Then a nurse came in and made me leave in order to give her an injection. Afterwards I came back and went on formulating that easy, transparent future. But she shook her head, murmured something and nothing more. Then the entire present was Gloria struggling to live—only she and I and the threat of death, only myself watching the flare of her nostrils that blessedly opened and closed, only this small room and the clock striking.

I took out a notebook and began to write this account. I would read it to her—to myself—when we were home again. Home again. How good that sounded! Nevertheless, it seemed very far away . . . as far away as rheumatism when one is twenty, as death was only yesterday. My attention wandered and I thought of the ball game today,

whether it would have been suspended because of rain . . .
of the English umpire making his debut in the stadium,
of the accounting entries I had made this morning. But
when she penetrated my thoughts, with her shiny, waxen
forehead, with her dry mouth chewing her fever, I felt
very alien to the Saturday that might have been mine.

It was eleven-thirty and I remembered God, remembered my ancient hope that He might exist. For reasons of
strict integrity, I didn't want to pray. One prays to the one
in whom one truly believes. I couldn't truly believe; I only
hoped that He might exist. Then I realized I wasn't praying
just to see if my integrity might not move Him. I prayed—
a shattering prayer, full of scruples, brutal; a prayer in
which there would remain no doubt that I didn't want to,
and couldn't, worship Him; a prayer of armed truce. I
was listening to my own mental stammering, but I heard
only Gloria's breathing, difficult, laborious. Another eternity
and the clock struck twelve. If she gets through today . . .
and she had gotten through it. She had definitely gotten
through it. She was still breathing. We both kept on
breathing and I fell asleep, dreamlessly.

Someone shook my arm and it was ten past four. She
wasn't there. Then the doctor came in and asked the nurse
if she had told me. I shouted, yes, that she had told me—
although it wasn't true—and that he was an animal, a
stupider fool even than the nurse, because he had said
that if she got through today, and nevertheless . . . I
shouted at him frantically. He looked at me in a kindly
way, in a hatefully understanding way. I knew that I was
mistaken: I was the guilty one for having gone to sleep, for
having left her without looking at her, without imagining
her future, without my wounding, pushing prayer.

And then I asked them to tell me where I could see
her. I was held up by a dull curiosity to see her disappear,
taking with her all my children, all my holidays, all my
apathetic tenderness toward God.

FAYAD JAMIS

A Cuban, although born in Zacatecas, Mexico, in 1930, Fayad Jamis has had two books of poetry published, *Los parpados y el polypo* and *Alumbran*. Many influences, including that of Vallejo, color the work of this young writer.

Sometimes

Sometimes, in the silence of the corridor, something springs,
somebody shatters a certain old name.
The maddened fly crosses, buzzing, burning,
far from the luminous spiderweb.
It is like this, so lonely, but so full of surprises.
Large house of childless ghosts where the dust
makes new windows, new furniture and dances.
No, you don't know it, you have not looked long in my
    pupils
and so yours fill with tears. Listen to me:
my house does not flee; it is distant always.
Up these stairs one rises into the blackness.
One tires of climbing them and falls asleep gasping,
knowing neither of days, nor of fever, nor the immense
    noise
of the city that seethes in the background.
Sometimes, in the silence of the corridor, someone is born
    suddenly,
someone who knocks on the unnumbered door and who
    calls.
No, you have never been there. No, you don't come here.
My word is to open, but it happens that almost always
I am traveling.

A veces

A veces, en el silencio del pasillo, algo salta,
rompe alguien algún viejo nombre.
La mosca enloquecida cruza zumbando, ardiendo,
lejos de la telaraña luminosa.
Esto es así, tan solo; pero tan lleno de sorpresas.
Caserón de fantasmas sin hijos, en que el polvo
hace nuevas ventanas, nuevos muebles y danzas.
No, tú no lo conoces, tú no me has visto mucho las pupilas
y por eso te llenas de lágrimas. Escúchame:
mi casa no se fuga; está lejos, siempre.
Por estas escaleras se sube hasta lo negro.
Uno se cansa de subirlas y jadeando se duerme
sin saber ni los días, ni la fiebre, ni el ruido inmenso
de la cuidad que hierve al fondo.
A veces, en el silencio del pasillo, alguien nace de pronto,
alguien que toca en la puerta sin número y que llama.
No, tú no has estado aquí jamás. No, tú no vengas.
Mi palabra es abrir, pero es que casi siempre
ando de viaje.

Dora Guerra

Born in Paris, France, in 1925, this young Salvadorean poet was awarded a government scholarship by her native country for study in Europe.

Tidings of Your Death

And I said it at last: "My father is dead."
And I did not know it.
I was clinging to my yesterday with my entire body.
To my yesterday luminous with his eyes,
sonorous with his voice,
quiet with his silence,
alive with his whole-bodied aliveness.
To my warm yesterday of his flame,
of his pale hands,
of his soft breath;
and also his naive necktie,
and his careless suit,
and the ring on his finger.

But yesterday, suddenly, I told myself:
You know? My father is dead.

And now I have understood it irremediably.
From all my unfinished hours,
from all not finding myself in mirrors,
from all words
filled with his silence,
I will receive the news that he has died,
and ever more will I know of his leaving
and never more of his return.

And now, from my emptiness, what will I do?
From my unseeing eyes,

130

from my thirst of winterless earth?
What will I do to find myself if I am alone,
if he does not come to my dreams?
What will I do to say one word
if he does not guide my accent?

But no. I have to say it now.
Now that it is my time.
Now, at last, that I have understood it:
now that he has died.

But what will I say if I do not remember?

                                        Ah, yes:

It was a blond afternoon one January,
a fresh happiness,
and a coming from afar.
A remark of your voice, and a "Now I understand."
A pointing of your hand toward the mountain
and a remark of my eyes, "Yes, now I see it."
And at times a laughing,
and at times a crying.

Ah, wonderful! Now I remember it:
Your look and mine
together on the pathways,
mounting to the highest part of the road,
running in the warm sunlight of the hill.
And the two of us, below,
agreeably sitting on the ground.

Afterward, your finger gravely lifted
to show me the name of a star.
And that first star of the evening
lighted our silence.

The greatest heart,
the most complete love.
The eyes knowing and the voice vacant,
the two of us returned along the path.
Our feet were walking
parallel in the shadows.

But now I know it:
                    my father is dead.

I told myself the news in the street
one day that I found myself without a memory.
Alone, already, without my cardinal points,
on the edge of time.

And I have understood it irremediably.

No longer will I know where one finds
the name of a star,
nor why the lightning bug glows,
nor the why of the lemon tree.
Nor the description of the birds,
nor how accents are placed.
No longer will I know how
windmills are broken,
nor what is the Latin for roses
and dead birds.

I can no longer . . .
                    Ah, what can I do now
if my body lacks members,
if my flesh weighs on me
because of his weightless bones?
If my body is dark, all mine,
and his transparent, and I see it not?

You, you I love,
with your two pale hands,
with your ring on your finger,
with your soft necktie,
with your small body.

You, you I love,
with the precise arc of your gesture,
with your well-defined yes,
and with your unqualified no.
It is all of you that I love.
Ah! Where are you that I do not find myself?

I told myself the news in the street,
and now I know it:

> My father is dead.

Noticia de tu muerte

Y lo dije por fin: "Mi padre ha muerto".
Y yo no lo sabía.
Me aferraba a mi ayer con todo el cuerpo.
A mi ayer luminoso de sus ojos,
sonoro de su voz,
quieto de su silencio,
vivo de su vivir de cuerpo entero.
A mi cálido ayer donde su llama,
donde sus manos pálidas,
donde su suave aliento;
y también la corbata candorosa,
y el tibio traje,
y el anillo en el dedo.

Pero ayer, de repente, me lo dije:
¿Sabes? mi padre ha muerto.

Y ya lo he comprendido sin remedio.
Para todas mis horas no cumplidas,
para todo no hallarme en los espejos,
para toda palabra
llena de su silencio,
ya tendré la noticia de que ha muerto,
y siempre más sabré de su partida
y nunca más de su regreso.

¿Y ahora qué haré yo desde mi nada?,
desde mis ojos ciegos,
desde mi sed de tierra sin invierno.
¿Qué haré para encontrarme si estoy sola,
si él no llega a mi sueño?

¿Qué haré para decir una palabra
si no guía mi acento?

Pero no. Tengo que decirlo ahora.
Ahora que es mi tiempo.
Ahora que por fin lo he comprendido:
ahora que él ha muerto.

¿Pero qué diré yo? si no recuerdo . . .
                                        Ah, sí:
Era una rubia tarde de un enero,
una fresca alegría,
y un venir desde lejos.
Un decir de tu voz, y un "ya comprendo".
Un señalar tu mano la montaña
y un decir de mis ojos "sí, ya veo".
Y a ratos un reir,
y a ratos un llorar . . .

¡Ah, qué bien! Ahora lo recuerdo:
tu mirada y la mía
juntas por los senderos,
subiendo a lo más alto del camino,
corriendo por el sol tibio del cerro
Y los dos, desde abajo,
dulcemente sentados en el suelo.

Después tu dedo gravemente alzado
para mostrarme el nombre de un lucero.
Y aquel primer lucero de la tarde
nos encendió el silencio.

El corazón más grande,
el amor más entero.
Los ojos sabios y la voz vacía,
regresamos los dos por el sendero.
Caminaban en sombra
nuestros pies paralelos.

Pero ahora lo sé:
                    mi padre ha muerto.
Yo me di la noticia por la calle

un día que me hallé sin un recuerdo.
Sola ya sin mis puntos cardinales,
en la orilla del tiempo.

Y ya lo he comprendido sin remedio.

Ya no podré saber dónde se encuentra
el nombre de un lucero,
ni por qué la luciérnaga se enciende,
ni por qué el limonero.
Ni cómo es el retrato de los pájaros,
ni cómo se colocan los acentos.
Ya no podré saber cómo se rompen
los molinos de viento,
ni cómo es el latín entre las rosas
y los pájaros muertos.

Yo no podré . . .
                    Ay, qué podré yo ahora
si estoy como sin miembros,
si me pesa mi carne
por sus livianos huesos.
Si mi cuerpo es moreno, todo mío
y el suyo transparente y no lo veo.

A ti, a ti te quiero,
con tus dos manos pálidas,
con tu anillo en el dedo,
con tu dulce corbata,
con tu cuerpo pequeño.

A ti, a ti te quiero,
con la curva precisa de tu gesto,
con tu sí bien trazado,
y con tu no todo entero.

A ti todo te quiero,
¡Ay! dónde estás que no me encuentro.

Yo me di la noticia por la calle,
y ahora ya lo sé:
                    Mi padre ha muerto.

Julio Cortazar

An Argentine national, born in Brussels, Belgium, in 1914 and now living in Paris, Cortázar rejects partisan labels for this self-appraisal: "little education, many influences, no affiliation." He is the author of two volumes of short stories, *Los reyes* and *Bestiario*, both published in Argentina, and is one of that country's outstanding younger writers.

The Gates of Heaven

At eight o'clock José Maria came with the news; without preliminaries he told me that Celina had just died. I remember noticing the phrasing—"Celina has just died"— a little as though she herself had decided the moment when it should happen. It was nearly nightfall, and José Maria's lips trembled when he told me of it.

"Mauro has taken it very hard. He was like a wild man when I left him. We'd better go."

I had to finish some notes. Besides, I had promised to take a girl to dinner. I made a few telephone calls and then left with José Maria to look for a taxi. Mauro and Celina lived at Canning and Santa Fé, so it took us about ten minutes from my place. As we approached we could see people already standing about the doorway, looking guilty and abashed. On the way I learned that Celina had begun to vomit blood at six, that Mauro had brought the doctor, and that his mother was with them. It seems that the doctor has just begun to write a long prescription when Celina opened her eyes and finished dying with a sort of cough —almost a hiss.

"The doctor had to leave quickly," José Maria said, "because Mauro wanted to hit him. I held Mauro. You know how he is when he gets mad."

I was thinking of Celina—of Celina's empty face waiting for us in the house. I scarcely heard the cries of the

136

old women and the commotion in the patio, but I do remember that the taxi cost two-sixty, and that the driver had a cloth cap. I saw two or three of Mauro's friends, who were reading *La Razón*, in the doorway. A little girl in a blue dress was holding a brown and white cat in her arms and carefully smoothing its whiskers. Further inside, the laments and funeral smells began.

"Go and see Mauro," I told José Maria. "See that he gets enough to drink."

They were preparing *mate* in the kitchen. The wake was organizing itself—the faces, the drinks, the heat. Now, so soon after the death, it was incredible how the neighborhood people dropped everything—even the listening to questions and answers—to gather at the scene. A *mate* straw gurgled loudly as I passed by the kitchen and peered into the funeral chamber. Missy Martita and another woman looked at me from the dark interior where the bed seemed to be floating in jelly.

"Poor little dead one," said Missy Martita. "Come in, sir. Come in and see her. She looks like she's sleeping."

Choking back an urge to swear at her, I entered the warm broth of the room. For a time I looked at Celina without seeing her, and then I let myself go to her, to the black, straight hair springing from the low forehead, which shone like mother-of-pearl on a guitar, to the empty white plate of her blank face. I realized that I had nothing to do there, that the room now belonged to the women and to the mourners coming in the night. Not even Mauro could enter peacefully to sit by Celina's side. Celina was not even there waiting. That black and white figure had gone over to the side of the mourners. It favored them with its eternally immobile theme. Better to go and look for Mauro who remained on our side.

From the chamber to the dining room there were deaf sentinels smoking in the unlighted passage: Peña, Crazy Bazán, Mauro's two younger brothers, and a nondescript old man who greeted me respectfully.

"Thank you for coming," one of the brothers said to me. "You've always been such a good friend to poor Mauro."

"You know who your friends are at times like this," said the old man, giving me a hand that felt like a live sardine.

All this was happening, but I was again with Celina and Mauro in Luna Park, dancing at the Carnival in 1942. Celina had been dressed in light blue, a color that went very badly with her complexion; Mauro was in a Palm Beach suit. I had six whiskies under my belt and an enormous thirst. I liked to go out with Mauro and Celina, to be close to their hard, hot happiness. The more I was reproached for my friendship with them, the more I clung to my days and hours with them in order to witness the existence of something of which they themselves were unaware.

I pulled myself back from the dance. A wail sounded from the chamber, rising through the doors.

"That must be the mother," said Crazy Bazán, almost happily.

"Perfect syllogism of the humble," I thought. "Celina dead, mother comes, mother wails." I was sick of thinking that way, *thinking* all the things that it was enough for others to feel. Mauro and Celina had not been guinea pigs to me. No I liked them—I still like them—very much. It was only that I could never enter into their simplicity; I had to nourish myself on the reflection of their blood. I am Dr. Harday, a lawyer discontented with the Buenos Aires law, music and race tracks; and as far as I am able, I move in other directions. I know that behind my dissatisfaction lies my curiosity, the notes that, little by little, fill my files. But not Celina and Mauro, not Celina and Mauro.

"Who would have thought this?" I heard Peña. "So fast . . ."

"Well, you know her lungs were bad."

"Yes, but just the same . . ."

They were defending themselves against the gaping earth. "Very bad lungs, but even so . . ." Celina must not have expected her death either: tuberculosis was only a "weakness" for Mauro and her. Again I saw her whirling enthusiastically in Mauro's arms—Canaro's orchestra up above, and an odor of cheap powder. Afterward she had

danced a *machicha* with me; the floor was a horror of
people and vapors.

"How well you dance, Marcelo," as though astonished
that a lawyer would be capable of following a *machicha*.
Neither she nor Mauro ever addressed me familiarly. I
used the intimate form with Mauro, but returned Celina's
formal treatment. It was hard for Celina to drop the
"Doctor," which was the title for any professional or well-
educated man. Maybe she was proud of using it in front
of others—"My friend, the doctor." I asked Mauro to tell
her I objected, and finally she began using "Marcelo." In
this way, they came a little closer to me, but I remained
as far away as before. Not even going together to public
dances, boxing or even football (Mauro had played with a
team called Racing years before), or drinking *mate* until
all hours in the kitchen diminished my isolation. When the
lawsuit ended and I won five thousand pesos for Mauro,
Celina was the first to ask me not to seclude myself, to
come and see them.

She was already ill. Her voice, always a bit hoarse,
was growing weaker. She coughed at night. Mauro bought
her Escay neurophosphate, which was idiotic, and Bisleri
iron quinine pills—things which some people find in magazine ads and have faith in.

We went to dances together, and I watched them live.

"You should talk to Mauro," said José Maria who had
suddenly sprung up beside me. "It will do him good."

I went, but I was thinking all the time of Celina. It
was an ugly thing to realize, but what I was really doing
was gathering and ordering my data about Celina, things
which were never written down but were stored well in my
memory. Mauro was crying openly, like any healthy animal
of this world, without the least shame. He took my hands
and wet them with his feverish perspiration. When José
Maria forced him to drink a gin, he swallowed it between
two sobs with a strange noise. And the words he spoke were
a mumbling of stupidities with all his life in them, all the
obscure consciousness of the irreparable thing that had
happened to Celina. The enormous narcissism was finally

free to make a spectacle of itself. I was sickened by Mauro but much more with myself, and I started drinking cheap cognac which scorched my mouth. Now the wake was moving at full speed; from Mauro down, they were all perfect. Even the night helped—warm and calm, pleasant for being in the patio and speaking of the dead woman, for letting the dawn arrive while we washed Celina's dirty linen in the dew.

That was on Monday. Afterwards I had to go to Rosario for a conference of lawyers where we did nothing but applaud one another and drink like fools. Then I returned for the weekend. Riding in the train were two dancers from the Moulin Rouge; I recognized the younger one, but she pretended not to see me. All that morning I had been thinking of Celina, not that her death mattered so much to me as the interruption of a system, of a necessary habit. When I saw the girls I thought of Celina's career and Mauro's gesture in taking her away from the Greek's.

It took courage to expect anything of Celina. It was in this period that I met Mauro, when he came to consult me about his mother's lawsuit over some land in Sanagasta. Celina accompanied him the second time, still wearing an almost professional makeup, swaying her hips, but holding tight to his arm. It was not hard for me to judge them, to taste the aggressive simplicity of Mauro and his unconfessed efforts to unite himself completely with Celina. When I began to deal with them it seemed that he had achieved this unity at least outwardly and in daily conduct.

Later, I judged more accurately. Celina escaped from him a little by means of caprices: her thirst for public dances, her long daydreams beside the radio with mending or knitting in her hands. When I heard her sing, I knew that at heart she was still with the Greek, far from a secure home, far from Mauro the shopkeeper. To know her better, I encouraged her cheap desires. The three of us went to many places with blinding loudspeakers, bubbling pizza and greasy papers on the floor. But Mauro preferred the patio, hours of conversation with the neighbors, and *mate*. He accepted grudgingly and submitted without surrendering.

Then Celina pretended to conform; perhaps she was getting used to going out less, to being a homebody. It was I who got Mauro to go to the dances, and I know she was grateful to me from the start. They loved each other, and Celina's happiness was enough for the two, sometimes for the three, of us. . . .

It seemed like a good idea to take a shower, telephone Nilda that I would come by for her Sunday on the way to the race track, and then go see Mauro. He was in the patio, smoking between lengthy *mates*. I was touched by two or three small holes in his shirt, and I clapped him on the shoulder by way of greeting. He had the same face as the last time, beside the grave, when he tossed in the handful of dirt and jerked back as if bewildered. But I found a clear glow in his eyes, his hand firm when I shook it.

"Thanks for coming to see me. Time drags, Marcelo."

"Do you have to go to the shop, or is someone taking your place?"

"I sent my brother, the cripple. I don't feel like going, even when the day lasts forever."

"Of course. You need distraction. Get dressed and we'll take a turn past Palermo."

"All right, it's the same to me."

He put on a blue suit with an embroidered handkerchief. I saw him put on perfume from a bottle that had been Celina's. I liked his way of tilting his hat, with the brim snapped up, and his light, jaunty, silent step. I resigned myself to listening to "you can see who your friends are at times like this," and with the second bottle of Quilmes Cristal he burst out with everything. We were sitting at a table in the rear of the cafe, almost by ourselves. I let him talk, but from time to time I served him beer. I scarcely remember everything he told me; I think that really it was always the same thing. One phrase remains—"I have her here"—and the gesture of stabbing his breast with his forefinger as though displaying a pain or a medal.

"I want to forget," he said also. "Anything—get drunk, go to a dance hall, forget . . . You understand me, Marcelo, you . . ." His forefinger rose enigmatically, doubled suddenly like a jackknife. In his condition he was ready to accept anything. When I happened to mention the Santa Fé Palace, he took it for granted that we were going to the dance; he was the first to get up and look at his watch. We walked without speaking, half dead from the heat, and all the time I suspected he was surprised at not feeling against his arm the warm happiness of Celina on the way to a dance.

"I never brought her to this place," he told me suddenly. "I was here before I knew her. It's a very tough place. Do you come here?"

In my files I have a good description of the Santa Fé Palace. It is no longer called Santa Fé, nor is it on that street. It's too bad that nothing of this sort can be described accurately—not the modest facade with its alluring posters and filthy box office, still less the loungers about the entrance who look one over from head to toe. What I remember next is worse, not because it is evil, but because there is nothing precise—only chaos, confusion resolving itself into a false order, hell and its circles. It was a real taxi-dance inferno, with a two-fifty entrance fee and fifty-cent women. There were poorly isolated compartments and a successive series of covered patios. In the first one there was a popular dance band with a soloist; in the second, a small combo with someone singing folk tunes; in the third, a northern musical group with singers and *malambos*. Standing in an intermediate passageway, we heard the three sets of music and saw the three circles dancing. One could choose which he preferred; or he could go from dance to dance, from gin to gin, looking for tables and women.

"It's not bad," said Mauro with his melancholy air. "A shame it's so hot. They should put in air conditioning."

Mauro spoke of refrigeration or of superheterodynes with the self-sufficiency of the Argentine who believes everything is due him. I took his arm and pushed him toward a table because he was still distracted, watching the bandstand and the singer who held the microphone with both hands and moved slowly to and fro around it. We relaxed slowly in front of two brandies; Mauro drank his with one swallow.

"This settles the beer. What a crowd in this dive!"

He called for another brandy, giving me a chance to ignore him and to look around. Our table was next to the dance floor. Along the other side there were chairs against a long wall and a group of women who came and went with the absent air taxi-dancers have when they work or play. There was not much talking; we could easily hear the orchestra, backed by accordions, playing with all its might. The singer was obstinately nostalgic with a gift for lending drama to what was essentially a fast, uninspired piece ". . . The tresses of my sweetheart I carry in my suit-case . . ."

I must admit that I come to this cabaret for the "monsters," and I know of no other where there are so many in one spot. They appear at eleven in the evening, coming in from obscure parts of the city, deliberately and surely by ones and twos—the women nearly dwarfs and very dark; the men resembling Javanese, squeezed into black or checked suits. The women have enormously high hairdos which make them more dwarf-like: hard, difficult coiffures that give a sensation of weariness and pride. The men these days frequently wear their hair loosely combed and high in the middle—enormous, effeminate tufts bearing no relation to the brutal faces below, to the expressions of lurking aggressiveness awaiting its hour, or to the efficient torsos set on slender waists. They recognize and admire each other silently, unexpressively. It is their dance and their gathering, their big night.

They come here; the monsters enfold each other with grave respectfulness; they gyrate slowly to piece after piece without speaking, many with their eyes closed, enjoying parity and completion at last. They recover in the intervals. At the tables they are arrogant and the women talk shrilly to attract attention. Then the males become fiercer, and I have seen one unleash a slap that twisted the face and tumbled the hairdo of a squint-eyed girl dressed in white and drinking anise. They also peroxide themselves: the dark girls raise rigid yellow cornfields above the muddy earth of their faces. They even practice blonde gestures, wear green dresses, convince themselves of their transformation, and condescendingly scorn the others who maintain their natural color.

Looking sidelong at Mauro, I studied the difference in his face with its Italian features, the face of the seaport dweller with no Negro or provincial intermixture, and I remembered suddenly that Celina was closer to the monsters, much closer than Mauro and I. I think that Kasidis had chosen her to please the most vulgar of his clientele. I had never been in Kasidis' place in Celina's time; but afterwards I went down there one night to see the place where she had worked before Mauro took her away. I saw nothing but whites, blonde or brunette, but white.

"I feel like dancing a tango," Mauro said plaintively. He was a little drunk as he started his fourth glass. I thought of Celina who would have been so much at home here, exactly where Mauro had never brought her. Now Anita Lozano accepted the loud applause of the audience as she waved from the bandstand. I had heard her sing at the Novelty when she was at her peak; now she was old and gaunt, but she still retained her tango voice—even better now because her style was vulgar and needed a voice a bit hoarse and muddy to go with the ranting lyrics. Celina had had such a voice when she had been drinking. Suddenly I realized how much the Santa Fé was Celina, the nearly insupportable presence of Celina.

To go off with Mauro had been a mistake. She bore it because she loved him and because he took her out of Kasidis' filth. But if she had not been forced to work in the dance halls, Celina would have loved to remain there. You could see it in her hips and in her mouth; she was built with the tango in mind, born from head to toe for cheap night life. That was why it was necessary that Mauro take her to dances. I have seen her transfigured at the first mouthfuls of hot air and the sound of accordions. Now, caught fast in the Santa Fé, I measured the greatness of

Celina, her bravery in paying Mauro with some years of cooking and sweet *mate* in the patio. She had renounced her taxi-dance heaven, her feverish vocation of anise and creole waltzes. As though she had consciously condemned herself for Mauro and Mauro's life, she barely imposed herself on his world that he might, sometimes, take her out to a party.

Now Mauro went by, clinging to a dark attractive girl, taller than the others, with a fine figure. His instinctive but deliberate selection made me smile; his little servant was the one least like the monsters. Then the idea returned to me that Celina had been in some way a monster like these, except that elsewhere and during the day it wasn't as apparent as it would have been here. I asked myself if Mauro would have noticed it; I was a little afraid of his reproach for bringing him to a place where memories grew from each thing like hairs on an arm.

This time there was no applause, and he drew near with the girl who suddenly became dull and gasping outside her tango.

"I'd like you to meet a friend."

We murmured the "pleased-to-meet-you's" of Buenos Aires and gave her a drink. I was happy to see Mauro getting into the swing of the evening, and I even exchanged a few words with the woman, who was called Emma—a name that doesn't suit a thin girl very well. Mauro seemed quite resolute and talked of orchestras with the short, sententious phrases that I admired him for. Emma ran on with the names of singers and memories of Villa Crespo and El Talar. Then Anita Lozano announced an old tango, and there were shouts and applause from the monsters, the men especially displaying unanimous enthusiasm.

Mauro was not so dazed as to have forgotten everything. When the orchestra opened with a wail of the accordions he looked at me suddenly, tense and rigid, as if he were remembering. I too saw myself in Racing: Mauro and Celina holding each other tightly in this same tango, which she later hummed all evening long, even in the taxi on the way back.

"Shall we dance?" Emma asked, drinking her grenadine noisily.

Mauro didn't even look at her. It seems to me that in this moment the two of us reached each other at the most profound depths. Now—now that I write—I can see only one image from my twenty years in Barracas Sporting Club: diving into the pool and meeting another swimmer at the bottom, both touching the bottom simultaneously and half-seeing each other in the green, bitter water. Mauro pushed his chair back and braced himself with an elbow on the table. He saw the dance floor as I did, and between the two of us Emma was lost and humiliated, though she tried to disguise it by eating French fries.

There was smoke coming from the next room where they were eating barbecued meat and dancing to ranch music; the roast meat and the cigarettes formed a low cloud that disfigured the faces and the cheap painting on the opposite wall. Mauro was supporting his chin with the back of his hand, staring fixedly ahead. Once or twice I saw Mauro glance at the bandstand where Anita was pretending to wave a baton, but again he fixed his eyes on the couples. I heard Emma say something, excuse herself, and the space of table between Mauro and myself was cleared, although we didn't look at each other.

A moment of immense happiness seemed to have descended on the dance floor. I breathed deeply as if to participate in it and I think I heard Mauro do the same. The smoke was so thick that the faces on the far half of the floor were diffused and we could not see the chairs reserved for the wallflowers because of the interposed bodies and the haze. Again the dancers became immobile. Celina, who was along the right side, emerging from the smoke and whirling obediently to the pressure of her partner, remained in profile to me for a moment, then turned her back and lifted her face to listen to the music. I say Celina, but then it was more a matter of knowing than of understanding Celina to be there crystal clear without being there.

The table trembled suddenly; I knew it was Mauro's

arm that trembled, or mine, but we weren't afraid; fear is something that is closer to dread than to happiness and the stomach. In reality it was stupid, a feeling of isolation that would not set us free, allow us to collect ourselves.

Celina remained there, without seeing us, drinking in the tango with that face which the yellow light of the smoke transfigured. Any of the brunettes could have looked more like Celina than she did in that moment. Happiness changed her atrociously; I wouldn't have been able to tolerate Celina as I saw her at that moment, in that tango. There remained in me enough intelligence to measure the devastation of her happiness—her face entranced and stupid in the paradise finally achieved. She could have been like that in Kasidis' place, had it not been for the work and the clients. Now in her personal heaven, nothing restrained her; she surrendered her whole being to joy and again entered the order where Mauro could not follow her. It was her hard heaven conquered; the tango played once more just for Celina.

I didn't want to look at Mauro. Then I collected myself. My cynicism returned. It all depended on how he took the thing; so I stayed as I was, studying the floor, which emptied little by little.

"You saw?" said Mauro.

"Yes."

"You saw how much she looked like Celina?"

I didn't answer. The relief weighed heavier than pity. He was on this side, the poor man was of this side and he couldn't reach a belief in what we had known together. I saw him get up and cross the floor with a drunkard's step, searching for the woman who looked like Celina. I sat quietly, slowly smoking a cigarette, watching him come and go, knowing he was wasting his time, that he would come back, worn and thirsty, without having found the gates of heaven in the smoke and the crowd.

Gonzalo Rojas

Author of two published volumes of poetry and professor of literary style and esthetics at Chile's University of Concepcion, Rojas was born in the seaport of Lebu in 1917.

Love

I

Suddenly you appear with your flame and your voice,
and you are white and supple, and you are there watching
   me,
and I want to turn from you, and you are there watching
   me,
and we are innocents, and the red tide
kisses me with your lips, and it is winter, and I am
in a harbor with you, and it is night.

And there are no sheets for sleeping, and there is no, there
   is no
sun in any place, and there is not one star
to wrench from the heavens, and lost,
we do not know what happens, why nakedness
consumes us, why the storm
cries like a mad woman, atlhough no one listens to it.

And now, exactly now that you are limpid—permit me—
now that I desire you and your voice seduces me
with its profound philtre, let me unite
my kiss with your kiss, let me touch you
like the sun, and die.

To touch you, to unite you to the day which I am, to sweep
   you up
to the high heavens of love, to those heights

where one day I was king, to carry you to the free wind of
    dawn,
to fly, to fly ten thousand, ten thousand years with you,
one minute only, but to keep on flying.

II

It is four o'clock, and death—this house is death—
already rises through my veins; asphyxia
beats at my window. It is the hour. Here I am
waiting for you afoot. I am the gentleman
you seek. Do not waver. It is my hour.

I do not tremble; here you have me; but give me a minute
of grace; let
the dawn carry my kiss and, with my kiss,
a thorn of blood to its mouth, the color
of my soul to its beauty,
that it may feed on me, and this which I am
may purify its lips more than burning coals
and from its lips may breathe my flames each day.

Look at her. A fragile thing, but I chose her
among all the daughters of woman, like God
His most pure star, that she might shine in the wind
of my great sacrifice. She does not seem to sleep.
Or scarcely to breathe. Or to be sad.

It is four o'clock. It is the hour. Tell her, oh Death, my
    farewell.
She is the one I love: my slender, fragrant sapling.
Her black hair spreads like a tree. The sea
opens a beach between her breasts. See
what is happening within her eyes: the train
carries her through a rapid wood. She is crying
because I do not go with her.
It is four o'clock, my Death. Tear me from this now,
rise to my heart. I am content
to enter you, afoot, like a conqueror of
the unknown sea.

III

Woman, we grow; we despair, growing,
obscurely, without childhood, more and more obscurely,
toward the only imminent beginning
where we will be reborn, where you
will be reborn for me alone.

For me, for no one else,
for my kisses, for my thirty mouths,
for my whirlwind where you learned one day
to fall swiftly like an errant star:
woman, my star, swiftly.

I do not insist on touching you merely to inflame you.
I am experienced: I love you.
I am violent: I love you even more deeply,
even beyond all deliriums
and, like them, I possess you implacably.

Oh unique flower: no one
saw in your nature the freedom of the day
as I saw. Nobody
knew how to decipher you, gentle corolla,
profound motherhood.

Mother of man, mother of the dreams of man,
possessed, pregnant by the frenzy of man,
by the innocence, by the sacrifice
of man.

Woman, time passes. I am a man. You
are a woman. Poetry
is our blood. All
that can be said of us is that,
and something more, useless
to repeat.

IV

Some months my blood was clothed with your beauteous
girl's figure, with your torrential

hair; and the sound
of your laughter, some months, made me weep the harsh
    thorns
of sadness. The world
began to die for me like a child in the night,
and I myself was a child burdened by my years, in the
    streets, a blind
angel, earthbound, darkened,
with my interior guilt, with your cruel beauty, and justice
plucking out my eyes for having looked at you.

And you soared free, lightly, over the sea, oh my goddess,
confident, perfumed,
because you were not guilty of your beauty, and joy
flowed from your mouth like a pure spring
of ivory, and you danced
with joyous steps of she-wolf, and in the vertigo
of the day, another girl
who was born of you, like another marvel
from the marvelous, wrote me a profoundly sad letter,
because we were far apart, and you said
that you loved me.

But the months fly by as the days fly, as fly
in endless flight, the tempests,
since nobody knows anything about anything, and every-
    thing
that we choose is confused, until we remain
alone, definitive, completely alone.

Wait there, child, stop there in the whirl
of the dance, like that once when I saw you approaching,
    my singular star.
I want to keep on seeing you many years; coming
impalpable, profound,
whirling thus, perfect, with your black dress
and your green kerchief and that waist, love,
and that waist.

Stay. Maybe you will turn to air,
or to light, but I say you will soar with me and with no
    other,
with him who now speaks to you of living forever,
you will soar to the sun, you will return
with him and with no other, one evening in June,
each three hundred years, by the edge of the sea,
eternal, eternally, with him, and with no other.

El amor

I

De pronto sales tú con tu llama y tu voz,
y eres blanca y flexible, y estás ahí mirándome,
y te quiero apartar, y estás ahí mirándome,
y somos inocentes, y la marea roja
me besa con tus labios, y es invierno, y estoy
en un puerto contigo, y es de noche.

Y no hay sábanas donde dormir, y no hay, y no hay
sol en ninguna parte, y no hay estrella alguna
que arrancar a los cielos, y perdidos
no sabemos que pasa, por qué la desnudez
nos devora, por qué la tempestad
llora como una loca, aunque nadie la escucha.

Y ahora, justo ahora que eres clara—permite—,
que te deseo, que me seduce tu voz
con su filtro profundo, permíteme juntar
mi beso con tu beso, permíteme tocarte
como el sol, y morirme.

Tocarte, unirte al día que soy, arrebatarte
hasta los altos cielos del amor, a esas cumbres
donde un día fuí rey, llevarte al viento libre de la aurora,
volar, volar diez mil, diez mil años contigo,
solamente un minuto, pero seguir volando.

II

Son las cuatro, y la muerte—esta casa es la muerte—
ya sube por mis venas, la asfixia
golpea a mi ventana. Es la hora. Aquí estoy
esperándote en pié. Yo soy el caballero
que buscas. No vaciles. Es mi hora.

No tiemblo, aquí me tienes, pero dame un minuto
de gracia, déjame
que la aurora le lleve mi beso y, con mi beso,
una espina de sangre a su boca, el color
de mi alma a su hermosura
para que se alimente de mi, y ésto que soy
purifique sus labios más que el carbón ardiendo
y por sus labios salgan mis llamas cada día.

Mírala. Es cosa frágil, pero yo la elegí
entre todas las hijas de mujer, como Dios
a su estrella más pura, para que arda en el viento
de mi gran desamparo. No parece dormir.
Ni respirar apenas. Ni estar triste.

Son las cuatro. Es la hora. Dile, oh Muerte, mi adios.
Es la que amo: mi espiga delgada y olorosa.
Su pelo negro crece como un árbol. El mar
abre una playa entre sus pechos. Mira
lo que pasa debajo de sus ojos: el tren
la lleva por un bosque veloz. Está llorando,
porque no voy con ella.
Son las cuatro, Mi Muerte. Sácame de ésto ya,
sube a mi corazón. Estoy contento
de entrar a ti, de pié, como conquistador
al mar desconocido.

III

Mujer: crecemos, nos desesperamos creciendo,
oscuros, sin infancia, cada vez más oscuros,
hacia el único orígen inminente

donde renaceremos, donde tú
renacerás para mí solo.

Para mí, para nadie
más que para mis besos, para mis treinta bocas,
para mi torbellino donde aprendiste un día
a caer velozmente como una estrella errante:
mujer, estrella mía, velozmente.

No me obstino en tocarte por sólo enardecerte.
Tengo experiencia: te amo.
Tengo violencia: te amo todavía más hondo,
todavía más lejos que todos los delirios
y, como ellos, te cobro posesión implacable.

Oh flor única: nadie
vió con tu naturaleza la libertad del día
como yo ví. Ninguno
te supo descifrar, apacible corola,
maternidad profunda.

Madre del hombre, madre de los sueños del hombre,
poseída, preñada por el furor del hombre,
por la inocencia, por el desamparo
del hombre,

Mujer, el tiempo pasa. Yo soy hombre. Tú
eres una mujer. La poesía
es nuestra sangre. Todo
lo que pueda decirse de nosotros es eso,
y algo más que es inútil
repetirlo.

IV

Unos meses la sangre se vistió con tu hermosa
figura de muchacha, con tu pelo
torrencial, y el sonido
de tu risa unos meses me hizo llorar las ásperas espinas
de la tristeza. El mundo
se me empezó a morir como un niño en la noche,

y yo mismo era un niño con mis años a cuestas, por las
    calles, un ángel
ciego, terrestre, oscuro,
con mi pecado adentro, con tu belleza cruel, y la justicia
sacándome los ojos por haberte mirado.

Y tú volabas libre, con tu peso ligero, sobre el mar, oh mi
    diosa,
segura, perfumada,
porque no eras culpable de haber nacido hermosa, y la
    alegría
salía por tu boca como vertiente pura
de marfil, y bailabas
con tus pasos felices de loba, y en el vértigo
del día, otra muchacha
que nacía de tí, como otra maravilla
de lo maravilloso, me escribía una carta profundamente
    triste,
porque estábamos lejos, y decías
que me amabas.

Pero los meses vuelan como vuelan los días, como vuelan
en un vuelo sin fín las tempestades,
pues nadie sabe nada de nada, y es confuso
todo lo que elegimos, hasta que nos quedamos
solos, definitivos, completamente solos.

Quédate ahí, muchacha, párate ahí, en el giro
del baile, como entonces, cuando te ví venir, mi rara estrella.
Quiero seguirte viendo muchos años, venir
impalpable, profunda,
girante, así, perfecta, con tu negro vestido
y tu pañuelo verde, y esa cintura, amor,
y esa cintura.

Quédate ahí. Tal vez te conviertas en aire,
o en luz, pero te digo que subirás con éste y no con otro,
con éste que ahora te habla de vivir para siempre,
tu subirás al sol, tú volverás
con él y no con otro, una tarde de junio,
cada trescientos años, a la orilla del mar,
eterna, eternamente, con él, y no con otro.

ERNESTO MEJIA SANCHEZ

This Nicaraguan poet journeyed to Spain, where he pursued his doctoral studies in literature at the University of Madrid, and he has also visited France, Italy, Mexico, Central America and the United States. Born in Masaya, the "City of Flowers," in 1923, he has published several volumes of poetry, including *Ensalmos y conjuros, La carne contigua* and *El retorno*. The following poem is from his anthology (1953).

The Recluse

The recluse is knowing in predictions,
in dreams, in secret words.
The recluse's heart is made of sand:
it grows damp with the rain.
The recluse does not suffer from memories:
he constructs his past like his future.
His heart is an hourglass.
The recluse has created love
in his image and likeness.
The recluse makes no comparisons.
The solitary one lies with death
and arises widower.
At night he purifies himself.
In limpid, deep, deep waters
he submerges himself.
The recluse knows not solitude:
the world accompanies him.

El solitario

El solitario es sabio en predicciones;
en sueños, en secretas palabras.

Es de arena el corazón del solitario:
se humedece con la lluvia.
El solitario no padece recuerdos:
construye el pasado como el futuro.
Reloj de arena es su corazón.
El solitario ha creado el amor
a su imagen y semejanza.
El solitario no hace comparaciones.
El solitario se echa con la muerte
y se levanta viudo.
Por las noches se purifica.
En limpias, profundísimas aguas
se sumerge.
El solitario no conoce la soledad:
el mundo lo acompaña.

RENE MARQUES

Versatility characterizes the creative work of this author of a volume of verse, a play and a collection of short stories. Born in Arecibo, Puerto Rico, in 1919, he has received grants from the Rockefeller Foundation (1949) to study drama at Columbia University and from the Guggenheim Foundation (1954-1955) to write a novel. The following story is a study of the Puerto Rican nationalist leader, Pedro Albizu Campos.

Give Us This Day

> . . . *sin otra luz ni guía*
> *sino la que en el corazón ardía.*
> SAN JUAN DE LA CRUZ

Eyes half-open, he looked up at the thick ausubo beams that held the brick roof. Moisture had stained them in blackish, irregular patterns. Bearing that heavy load for two centuries, he thought drowsily . . . and how many centuries had the great trees stood before they were felled to make the beams? Perhaps two centuries. Two centuries in the virgin forests of the island hills. When even the forests were undefiled . . . when there were forests . . . four centuries. The ausubo trees must have been feeble saplings when the great discoverer first set foot upon the shore. Four centuries. The history of the nation.

He opened his eyes and studied the monotony and symmetry of the rows of dark beams. For a few seconds his mind held the thought of that last word, nation. But almost unconsciously he murmured: "Built for eternity."

The sound of his voice startled him. He sat up in bed. The word "eternity" seemed to hang in the moist air of the room . . . *"for a thousand years in thy sight are but as yesterday when it is past, and as a watch in the night. . . ."*

There was the crucifix. The body of the man on the cross, crudely carved from soft wood, was grotesquely twisted. He smiled as he remembered how many eyes had turned away in disgust from that Christ in the agony of death. But it is beautiful, he thought. Rough country hands carved it for me. Then an afterthought: the hands of my brothers, from the wood of my native soil.

Suddenly he threw off the sheet that covered his lean body, and felt a shudder of unexpected dread. His right foot rested upon his left. His gaunt bare legs were united, the thighs meeting the torso in a pose of violent contortion. Again he looked at the crucifix and at the beams. From up there, his body on the bed must look like a Christ in the agony of death.

"Master, you have the countenance of Christ."

The words he had heard so many times were heard again as if just pronounced. Thank you, God, for this new day you have added to my life. And he prayed piously, his eyes tightly closed to shut out the four centuries of history that held up the load of Spanish brick.

A cool draft from the balcony chilled his half-naked body.

"Amen," he said aloud and stood up.

He went to the washbasin and doused his face. He had forgotten to change the water, but its coolness on his weary eyelids gave him a feeling of well-being, so he was not bothered by the fact that it was not very clean. He wiped his face carefully, as if accomplishing a difficult and complicated task. He tried to smooth his gray, curly hair with his fingers. Thank you for this new day . . .

He looked around. Time seemed to be held still in the humble, monkish room: the iron bed, the washbasin, the oil lamp on the mahogany night stand. Was it last month they cut off the electricity? The high ceiling, the wide door, the thick walls: they were built for eternity. He looked again at the crucifix carved by rough, country hands—a brother's hands, the wood of my native soil.

A loud noise shook his nerves. It was a combination of indescribable sounds—a roar of motors, a vehement grinding of gears and pulleys, a metallic pounding of monstrous drums. Time, held still in the washbowl, the iron bed, the grotesque crucifix, the ausubo beams, wavered before the brutal onslaught of this inexorable force. Apprehensively he looked toward the balcony.

"I won't go and look," he told himself. "I won't go." But a diabolical compulsion drew him to the open door.

The balcony was narrow. It was not necessary to go to the railing to look down on the street. The monster was there below. Over the ancient cobblestones, damp with rain, rolled the gray steel machine. Sunlight had not yet penetrated into the narrow street, and in the gloom of early morning, the thing looked like a military tank in momentary repose. Two men wearing thick gloves were emptying the contents of garbage cans into the monster's gullet. They worked silently, as if they were part of the mechanism that swallowed and noisily ground up the garbage in its bowels, to disgorge it later on the city dump.

Every morning he watched the operation with the same horrible fascination. The garbage truck with its dynamic lines, its unerring mechanism and noisy digestion suggested the destructive forces that threatened everything he loved.

"Understand clearly whence comes the demon to strike his blows, and make off with his body, and break his head." His eyes shone with a strange, deluded light.

The garbage truck moved on, taking its efficient digestive tract to a neighboring street. The first rays of sun found the rain-bright cobbles.

He looked up, across the city. It was the old quarter— ancient buildings of brick and stone, balconies of wrought-iron like the black lace of old mantillas, and broad, flat, sun-drenched roofs, and in the background, the somber beauty of the Spanish fortress. He spread his arms as if to gather the beloved city to him. He would have kissed every tile, every stone. He wanted to take the old city to his breast, soothe it with archaic lullabies and protect it from dangers that threatened to destroy it.

A light flashed and hurt his eyes. That again, he thought, looking darkly towards the tower. It was the sun reflecting from the top of the tower. Tall, offensive, made of steel, the tower rose arrogantly above the old buildings that surrounded it. At the top was a series of intricate glittering objects. "The Naval Station Tower." He repeated it aloud, as if to explain to himself the inexplicable. He did not understand the reason for the hostile artifact. He did not understand at all. A signal tower, perhaps. But those intermittent lights, were they reflections of the sun, or were they luminous rays sent out by the thing itself? Why does it always have to strike my room, he thought. He moved to the left of the door to protect his eyes from the rays.

With implacable clarity the sunlight now revealed to him details that he had not seen before: the net of the telephone cables and electric wires, like a web coarsely woven by a lazy spider; the lamp posts, standing like slaves perpetuated in the public service; the skyscraper of a foreign bank, hurling its menacing shadow over the docile colonial houses; the cold modern Hotel Metropolitano, where blond tourists slept off the intoxication of their latest follies.

The black smoke of a factory began to soil the clean sky. The beloved city escaped him as a thousand other people began to engage in their noisy business.

"Good morning, master."

The voice was young and harsh, but with a note of tender respect. At the window of the house across the street, the young neighbor was combing his hair with a green comb. On his face was a frank, broad smile.

"Good morning, my son," he smiled and waved. "Did you sleep well?"

"Very well, master, and you?"

The same greeting every morning. Who was it? He didn't know. Probably always lived there. But he had not noticed until the enforced loneliness of these last months.

He remembered one day when they had forgotten to bring his dinner, the young man had brought a package of cold meat and handed it to one of the guards. "It is for the man upstairs. He can't go all day without eating," he had said. When he had seen the boy at the window the next morning, he had tried to express his gratitude, but his benefactor had pretended not to hear, and remarked how hot it had been the night before.

Why does he call me "master"? He is not one of mine. I don't know him. Besides, he is very young. Almost a child. And he thought of his son. A refugee in a foreign land. He tried to recapture the image of his absent son's face. But he could see nothing but the broad smile on this bright, dark face, the features of his young neighbor. So many years, oh, God, so many years. He concentrated. He tried to force his memory to respond to his desire. A loved one lost to memory—how horrible!

"Until later, master." The young man moved away from the window so that he could not be seen from the street below. Winking maliciously, he lowered his voice: "The faithful friends of the night are leaving, but here are the daytime friends." Then he disappeared, smiling.

It was so. Four new guards were coming to relieve the night watch. The new arrivals stationed themselves on the sidewalk under his balcony, and the others went sleepily away. They will not be able to enjoy their children today. They will have to sleep all day so they can come back tonight. They will lose the blessing of another day. He watched them go. As they turned the corner, the sunlight glistened on the barrels of their rifles. He went out onto the balcony and stood at the rail.

"Good morning, boys."

The new guards answered cordially. Tight, lustrous uniforms molded their athletic bodies. Good soldiers, he thought, pleased. The officer, a serious young lieutenant, had come forward to stand directly beneath him. The lieutenant could not conceal a certain nervousness as his young face looked upward.

"You shouldn't go out on the balcony without a shirt." The lieutenant had intended his voice to sound authoritative, but his inflection gave the words a tone of entreaty.

"You are right. Excuse me. I hadn't noticed." He smiled

at the lieutenant and went inside. He was unaccountably upset. He could not imagine how he could have appeared like that in public. He felt as guilty and ashamed as a little child caught in some offense. "Master, you look like a great lord of the last century." He looked at his shirt hanging on the back of the cane-bottomed chair, his black silk tie, his dull black shoes.

He began to dress methodically, smoothing out the wrinkles in his shirt. He knotted the tie in a large, old-fashioned bow, carefully concealing the frayed parts. "I like what there is in you of other ages." Her voice came back to him with a rush of tenderness. He put on his shoes; the dull spots on the dark leather disgusted him. He tried to remove them with a piece of newspaper. Then he washed his hands. I must change the water, he thought. He smoothed his rebellious hair and groomed his mustache. He was ready. Then he stopped, motiveless.

Where was he going? Going? He looked around dismayed, and noticed the old books. There remained only a few dozen; thousands of volumes were now in friendly hands. Time had almost erased the golden titles. He had read them a hundred times. He knew them by heart—not merely the printed words, but his own marginal notes, penciled in his cramped, irregular hand. He touched the small, red leather volume that bore Juan's inscription.

Until September, Juan had come every day. Of course, they subjected him to a thorough search in the entrance hall. Before he could be allowed to go upstairs, they had to make sure that his hands and pockets were empty. But Juan brought news, messages of encouragement from friendly voices, valuable knowledge. After September, they had forbidden even his visits. The last consolation was to see him pass by the house every afternoon. They would greet one another silently, and Juan would move slowly down the street, turn the corner and disappear. What anxiety there had been in the eyes of his friend as he gave that silent greeting! Then suddenly Juan no longer passed by. What had happened? He never knew.

Juan, my faithful Juan. Forcing back the unhappy

memory, he went to the chest, and opened the top drawer. The flag was carefully folded, resting on a pile of worn, neatly pressed clothes. *"For the Lord will not cast off his people, neither will he forsake his inheritance."* He lifted the flag and touched it softly to his cheek. *"And the rains descended and the floods came, and the winds blew and beat upon the house, and it fell not; for it was founded upon a rock."* He felt happy and at peace. He unfolded the flag and hung it on the iron bedstead. Then he sat on the cane-bottomed chair. He sat still in quiet, intense contemplation. On the mildewed plaster wall above the bed, above the flag, was the shield of the miserable island— rampant lions guarding secular castles, the double yoke imposed upon the mortal force of vengeful arrows, the Cross of Jerusalem of the triumphant Crusades, and the white lamb, immaculate, reclining upon the Book of God. . . . *"And he shewed me a pure river of water of life, clear as crystal, proceeding out of the throne of God and of the Lamb."* The standard of the Christian peace floated above the green scutcheon, anchor of hope. And the Latin device proclaimed the catholicism of its name: *Joannes Est Nomen Ejus.*

Juan, Juan, where are you? The memory of his friend's sorrowful look made him close his eyes. The river of life which proceeded out of the throne of the lamb spilled upon the flag, and the blood of martyrs spilled over the blue abyss onto the whiteness of the sacred wool.

He had not come to bring peace. "We will die for you, master." No, not for him. For the deep roots of the race that evil hands sought to profane; for the land that nourished the sacred root; for the tongue of our fathers; for the Cross of the Redemption; for liberty. Not for him. But he had seen their blood flow, and the blood of their enemies. Blood and violence had been the wake of his tragic passage. "Assassin!" Some thought it was easy. Easy? *"Oh, strait is the gate and narrow is the way which leadeth unto life, and few there be that find it."* And he saw the white star of the flag on the blue triangle of an immutable trinity—love, life, death. Could it have been otherwise? God's people have crossed rivers of blood to reach their salvation. The sword of any liberator is stained with his brother's blood. And his words tasted of blood, too. He felt his heart drenched in blood . . . the interminable ranks of young faces with pale cheeks and bright eyes. The eyes are the torches of the soul.

Her eyes had reflected centuries of sorrow. So many years—oh, God, so many years. He remembered her face as he had seen it a few moments before they parted. You must leave the country, go to our son; I will stay here alone. And she had obeyed without question, without tears, without a word. He remembered the straight, dark hair framing her forehead and cheeks; the eyes—not even moments of triumph could erase their sadness—the finely molded mouth, the lips firmly closed, accustomed to guard the secrets of a life filled with danger. It was impossible to imagine that mouth smiling. But he knew that she had smiled. He knew there had been a time when she laughed, the laughter of a woman happy and in love. He knew but he could not recall, he could not recapture a single smile. His ears were deaf to the sound of the laughter that his mind obstinately refused to forget.

He stood up quickly. The dark balcony was a frame for the blinding light from the street. Light! More light to counteract the light that blinded him. He thought of the trial and conviction, already imminent. They were only waiting to collect all the evidence. Then the official arrest. Then prison. Prison again, always prison. Far away he heard the hoarse blast of a tourist ship entering the harbor. Behind the mahogany nightstand a rat gnawed the old floorboards. He began to walk nervously from the light to the shadow.

Was this all? He looked at the crucified Christ. *"Thou shalt sow, but thou shalt not reap; thou shalt tread the olives, but thou shalt not anoint thyself with oil. . . ."*

He wondered what time it was, and smiled at himself. What did it matter? What does time matter to me? The sunlight advanced slowly, inexorably from the door to the center of the room. And with it the intermittent flash of

the steel tower advanced, too. Are they only reflections?
Could they be light rays? Fatal rays, perhaps? No. *They*
are too civilized to believe in the death penalty.

Was this the end of his mission? He looked at the
lamb on the shield and at the white star in the flag. I have
not come to bring you peace! Prison is peaceful. Why must
the end be so absurd? Why had his mission been lost in
time and space? Suddenly he stopped walking. The questions hammered insistently in his head. Why had he
stopped? What did it mean, this terrible anguish rising in
his throat, this obscure fear nailing him to the spot?

The sunlight, gaining ground against the shadows,
touched the antique sword on the chest. Its Toledo blade
had gleamed with blood in the triumphs of a long-past,
heroic age. Now it rested beneath a cloak of rust, outdated,
useless, still. "I love what there is in you of other ages,"
she had said. The sunlight was on his head. "Master, you
have the countenance of Christ." An implacable anguish
tightened his throat. The black tie seemed to strangle him;
feebly he tried to loosen the knot. The horn blast of a
large automobile sounded in the narrow street. Suddenly
he knew that something inevitable and terrible was happening to his mind. "My kingdom is not of this world." He
almost shouted; "I do not belong to this age I live in!"

The tension of his body, readying itself for the shock of
revelation, was so great that for a moment he thought he
would be torn apart. Panting, sweating, heartsick, dreading
to understand, finally unresisting, he accepted the fact: he
lived in an age that was not his own.

An obscure fear seized him. God, my God, give me
death. But death, which he had often unleashed against
others, would not come.

With violence and hatred he had lashed out at a world
silently industrious and resignedly sad. He had wanted to
revive romantic dreams and heroic ideals for a world in
which an ideal could hardly survive each day. He had left
an imprint and a testimonial, but he could do no more.
*"Thou shalt sow, but thou shalt not reap; thou shalt tread
the grape, but shalt not drink the wine."* Why had he been

so blind? Why? The past lived in him. And he saw clearly that his mission was not for this age of hostility but for the past. Why live? But death still did not answer his call. The trial and conviction would not bring death. They are too civilized to believe in the death penalty—he said it again, bitterly. He stood in the sunlight now, and the light was more painful than the dark.

Picking up his silver-headed cane, he left the room and crossed the inhospitable, empty parlor. In the hallway, he put on the old, black felt hat. As he descended the steep stairway, his spirit was calm and his mind at peace. *"Blessed are they which are persecuted for righteousness' sake: for theirs is the kingdom of heaven. . . ."* When he reached the lower hall, his look was serene, his smile tranquil.

He stepped out onto the sidewalk and saw the astonishment of the four soldiers. "Tired of guard duty, boys?" Without waiting for a reply he started down the street. Now they will shout "Halt!" He would pretend not to hear the order. God, let their aim be good. Luckily the street was deserted. There would be no innocent victims. For the first time in his life, he was risking his own blood.

He thought about his young neighbor. What would he say about it? He thought again about his own son in exile. He will be proud, he thought, smiling. "I will die before you," she had said. But she would outlive him, her lips tight, her eyes eternally sad. He thought of Juan. Juan, my faithful friend, we shall be together. Together again. The iron balconies, like the lace of old mantillas, hung over the street. The sun heated the cobbles between the somber, ancient houses, built for eternity. He heard the cathedral bells telling the hour. Why didn't death come?

Then he heard the firm footsteps behind him. Here it comes, here it comes. He stopped, holding his breath. He fixed his gaze on the black cross of a telephone pole and repeated to himself the words of the Saviour: *"Into thy hands I commend my spirit."* A voice broke the silence. "Master!" The name sounded strange, almost absurd. Slowly he turned around.

Before him stood the grave young lieutenant. He could not conceal his amazement. Had it been he who called, "Master?" He looked at the lieutenant's empty hands. The pistol rested peacefully in its leather holster. Back there, under the balcony, the other three soldiers remained at their posts, shouldering their rifles. He felt uneasy. Anxiously he sought the eyes of the young officer and discovered there a look of miserable supplication. At last he understood the truth: it was no use; death would not come. His hand closed on the cane. He wanted to strike, to violate that passivity, provoke disaster, make death inevitable. But his eyes met that entreating look again. He will not kill me; he would overcome me by force, but he would not kill me. It was then he felt the weight of his years. As never before he tasted the bitterness of age. The weariness of centuries weighed upon his back. Very old and very tired, he seemed to shrink before the athletic lieutenant.

"Did you want something?" (I want to die, he thought, but he did not say it.) "It is not necessary for you to leave the house. If you want something, I'll bring it to you myself."

What was he saying, this young man so full of life? It didn't matter what he was saying. The conflict behind his solicitude was very clear. They had given him custody of an old man. Kindness and embarrassment alternated in the face of the serious young officer. He does me the favor of calling me "Master." Through sudden tears he looked with sad gratitude into the eyes of his reluctant antagonist. The young neighbor who greeted him every morning, and Juan—had they, too, felt only pity for an unhappy old man? Oh, no, God, spare me this last humiliation.

With great difficulty, he began to walk back. The silver-headed cane, once a symbol of arrogance, was necessary now. The lieutenant approached him. Was he going to offer his arm? No, he has too much tact for that.

At the door of the house again, he saw the rifle barrels resting on the shoulders of the other guards. Death would not come from here, either. And he began to climb the stairs. Step by step, the shadows began to take possession of his soul. Upstairs, he hung the black felt hat on the hall rack and passed through the empty, inhospitable house. The tapping of the cane seemed to echo the rhythm of the ausubo beams. He went into his room. On the mahogany nightstand, next to the oil lamp, was his lunch. They had brought it while he was outside. They are incapable of killing me. But they give me my bitter, daily bread, bread for the belly. But the bread and the belly would be destroyed only by God. He looked at the evangelical lamb on the shield and at the lone white star in the flag.

He went to the bed, and laid his cane on the rumpled sheets. He took down the flag and folded it slowly, ceremoniously. Then he carried it to the chest. Before he put it back in its place, he held it against his cheek. He felt that he was breathing something of his own life into the flag. Finally he replaced it on top of the worn, neat clothes in the drawer.

He took the washbowl from its stand, and threw the dirty water into the deserted patio. The water fell with a long murmur, striking the ground like the final amen of a prayer. He put the bowl back in its place and filled it with fresh water from the jug. He stretched the towel carefully on the rack. Then he sat in the laurel chair.

He looked from the crucifix to the cane on the bed, then at the green scutcheon on the wall, the food cooling on the nightstand near the oil lamp with its blackened globe, the basin and the towel rack, the chest, and last, at the useless rusty sword. *Oh, strait is the gate and narrow is the way that leads to death. . . .* Time no longer held still in the room. It went its way in spite of the Christ, the iron bed, the blackened globe, the washbowl, the Spanish sword. How weary he was. His body was heavy with fatigue. How difficult it is to die, how difficult.

If only he knew the truth about tomorrow. Another trial, and then prison. Was that all? The useless sword cast a long thin shadow on the chest. *"Take therefore no thought for the morrow, for the morrow shall take thought for the things of itself. . . ."* It is true, he thought. *"Sufficient unto the day is the evil thereof."* And he sat still, his head bowed, staring at the sword of another century, waiting for death to come.

—CATHERINE RANDOLPH

Elba Fabregas

A native of Buenos Aires (born in 1922) and author of one
published volume of verse, this young Argentine poet here con-
jures up a nightmare world of surrealist imagery.

Demented Stone

I

The walls are white, yellow, violet;
the floors are wood, dirty, clean.
Where is my chair that I may sit in my lap
caressing my hands?
Where my portraits,
my table filled with events?
Ah, this patience
I have upon my arms and my legs.
Dismembered silence.
Clear omen of the flight that commenced in my wings.
When will I spill my message of giddy blood?
Why am I here?
What do I do?
What do I want?
What do I wait for?
I have begun to be nothing so early.
The earth sprouted me like a plant with tremendous roots.
Pull me up;
draw off this sap;
grind me up for the fire;
return me to the ashen body of the tree trunks;
use my fruits, eat them or kill their sweetness.
The flowers weigh upon my temples;
gather them and go put them on the dead.
These leaves that sprout from my breast
are too much covering;

171

use them to arrange the bottoms of baskets
that you will fill with fruit.
Frighten those birds for me,
I am sleepy.
I cannot endure the seasons
because they hurt me so.
If nature would give me water
I would be a floating plant, lacking a destiny
Think of a name by which to know me again.
Destroy my other form
which may resemble that of an anemone.
Kindle in my eyes the light which illuminates the night.

II

Reach me that sob, I want to see it closely.
My heart rocks in my throat,
leaving on the ground a slanting sensation.
This bed, this sack of lamentation,
this skin of vinegar, this shroud,
this canvas of fever that oppresses me,
this icy vest that binds me.
The ceiling slowly in huge drops
of lime penetrates my face.
Reach me that laugh, I want to see it closely,
untie my feet before I burn.
All know I cannot launch myself
from the depth to the edge of my soul.
Let not the bread choke me, it has no flavor;
the water escapes down my back,
the sheet is opened and it scours me,
between water and road there is a greater distance.
Let the flowers hurry to grow between my teeth
broken by the spoon or crumbled by anguish.
The apple watches me from its red sex,
I have bitten into the peeling to see if I am inside.
My bed has bars,
its spread is the winter—gray rag with trimming.
The procession I have

is a long plain of piety, of succor,
of muffled blows in sand.
Reach me that sob, I want to see it closely,
and I shall laugh at your tears.

Piedra demente

I

Las paredes son blancas, amarillas, violetas;
los pisos de madera, sucios, limpios.
Dónde está mi silla para quedarme en el regazo mío
acariciándome las manos.
Dónde mis retratos,
mi mesa llena de acontecimientos.
Oh esta paciencia
que tengo sobre los brazos y las piernas.
Silencio desmembrado.
Claro anuncio del vuelo que comenzó en mis alas.
Cuándo volcaré mi mensaje de sangre vertiginosa.
Por qué estoy aquí.
Qué hago,
qué quiero,
qué espero.
He comenzado a ser nada tan temprano.
El suelo me brotó como una planta de tremendas raíces.
Arráncame;
quítame esta savia;
muéleme para fuego;
retórname al cadáver ceniciento de los troncos;
ocúpate de mis frutos, cómelos o mátales la dulzura.
Las floras me pesan sobre las sienes;
júntalas y vé a ponérselas a los muertos.
Estas hojas que me brotan sobre el pecho,
son demasiado abrigo;
prepara con ellas los fondos de los canastos
que llenarás de fruta.
Espántame estos pájaros,

tengo sueño.
No puedo soportar las estaciones
porque me duelen mucho.
Si la naturaleza me diera agua,
sería una flotante planta sin destino.
Piensa un nombre para que me conozcan de nuevo.
Acaba mi otra forma
que podría parecerse a la de una anémona.
Enciéndeme en los ojos la luz que ilumine la noche.

II

Alcánzame ese llanto, quiero verlo de cerca.
Mi corazón se mece en la garganta,
oblicua sensación deja en la tierra.
Esta cama, este saco de lamento,
esta piel de vinagre, esta mortaja,
esta lona de fiebre que me aprieta,
este chaleco helado que me ata.
El cielo raso lento en goterones
enormes con su cal entra en mi cara.
Alcánzame esa risa, quiero verla de cerca,
desátame los pies antes que arda.
Todos saben que no podré arrojarme
desde el fondo a la orilla de mi alma.
Que no me ahogue el pan, no tiene gusto,
el agua se me va por las espaldas,
la sábana está abierta y me socava,
desde ella al camino hay más distancia.
Apúrense las flores a crecer en mis dientes
rotos por la cuchara o deshechos de angustia.
La manzana me mira desde su sexo rojo,
he mordido la cáscara por ver si estaba dentro.
Mi cama tiene rejas,
su colcha es el invierno—trapo gris con la franja.
El cortejo que tengo
es una larga pampa de piedad, de socorro,
de golpes en la arena.
Alcánzame ese llanto, quiero verlo de cerca,
a lo mejor me río de tus lágrimas.

IDEA VILARINO

In addition to four volumes of verse—*La suplicante* (1945), *Cielo cielo* (1947), *Paraiso perdido* (1949) and *Por aire sucio* (1951)—this Uruguayan author has also published a collection of essays. She was born in Montevideo in 1920.

To Pass By

I want and don't want
I seek
a black air a flashing
slime a halt
an absolute hour mine now forever.
I want and don't want
I hope
and don't
and I despair
and for a while draw apart
with whole forgetting whole abandon whole
happiness
that entire disdain
that flight that more
that dismissed plea that emptiness
beyond love and
its precarious gift its no its forgetting
that unique door
the only paradise.
I want and don't want
I want
I want yes and how I want
to leave off being thus
to forget forever
to turn and pass by
not to smile

175

to leave
in a somber party
in a hard light
in a closed air
in a stately measure
in an invulnerable completed figure.

Pasar

Quiero y no quiero
busco
un aire negro un cieno
relampagueante un alto
una hora absoluta mía ya para siempre.
Quiero y no quiero
espero
y no
y desespero
y por veces aparto
con todo olvido todo abandono toda
felicidad
ese desdén entero
esa huída ese más
esa destituída instancia ese vacío
más allá del amor
de su precario don de su no de su olvido
esa puerta sin par
el solo paraíso.
Quiero y no quiero
quiero
quiero sí y cómo quiero
dejarlo estar así
olvidar para siempre
darme vuelta pasar
no sonreir
salirme
en una fiesta grave

en una dura luz
en un aire cerrado
en un hondo compás
en una invulnerable **terminada figura.**

Sebastian Salazar Bondy

The considerable literary output of this gifted young writer—
four volumes of verse, three plays, two poetry anthologies and
a volume of short stories—has been published chiefly in Peru
and Argentina. He was born in Peru's capital city of Lima in
1924.

I'm Sentimental

Cecilia arrived fifteen minutes after the appointed
time, just when my impatience, a strange mixture of fear
and pity, was about to become anguish. My mission on
that cloudy, melancholy July morning was neither easy
nor comfortable, and I knew it.

We took a taxi immediately. During the short trip we
exchanged only a few conventional phrases. Ceci had accepted, no doubt through weakness of character, that it
should be I, Gustavo's patient friend, who would accompany
her in this critical moment. Otherwise, she would not have
had courage to face the situation alone.

At the door of the house she told me timidly:

"You aren't under any obligation, Quique. If you don't
want to come in you don't have to. . . ."

She was pale and, now I can admit it, exciting. I felt
an urge to be tender with her, especially so that she would
not feel forsaken. I think, also, it was because I liked her.
However, I suppressed the perverse idea of taking advantage of the occasion for less generous ends than those
that had been proposed.

"No, Ceci, no," I answered, taking her hand affection-
ately. "Friends have to be of some use."

She smiled at me, closing her eyes, and that satisfied
me. I was not nervous. I rang the bell and the door opened

instantly. A young man of about twenty-two appeared on the threshold. It was I who spoke.

"Mrs. Rojas, please," I said.

The boy looked at us reflectively. Then, as though remembering something, he exclaimed, "Oh, yes! Come in, come in. . . ."

He led us through a corridor into a dark living room, its windows closed off by heavy red curtains. There were some easy chairs with velvet cushions, a small table on which there were magazines, and a piano.

"Sit down," he suggested pleasantly. "Mama will be here right away."

Cecilia sat down in an easy chair. Far away from her, I devoted myself to looking at the pictures hanging from the walls. In one of the frames was a faded medical diploma dated 1915.

"This is horrid, Quique," Cecilia said, as if to herself.

I approached her.

"Don't be nervous, Ceci," I told her with strained good humor. "Just close your eyes and jump in."

I suspected she was crying, but I preferred to ignore it because I was conscious of my responsibility. He didn't come with her because he's a coward, I thought. I looked at Cecilia obliquely. Now she was leafing through a magazine without noticing the pages. A distant tremor flowed from her slight body and made it vibrate subtly. I heard steps.

The door opened and the boy came in again. He addressed me.

"Excuse me, sir," he hesitated. "You have to pay in advance."

I put my hand in my pocket and pulled out the five bills of a hundred *soles* that Gustavo had given me the night before.

"Is a woman worth five hundred bucks?" he had asked as he gave them to me.

"Thank you," the boy said sweetly on receiving the money, adding, "Mama will be right in. Sit down." And he left.

Ceci was standing up. After a pause, she asked, "Will it be dangerous?"

I took her hand again. It was cold, moist.

"No. You'll be through it in half an hour. Are you afraid?"

She had no time to answer me. A fat woman about fifty years old, dressed in a white smock, entered the room. She came rubbing one hand against the other, and she gave off a penetrating odor of disinfectant.

"Good morning," she said, smiling.

We did not answer.

"Recommended by Dr. Jimenez?"

I answered yes.

"He told me that he had prepared you," she said, addressing Cecilia. "He is a magnificent doctor."

"He examined me," she answered in a wavering voice.

"This cannot be done every day," the fat woman said, "because it is very dangerous. Yes, children, very dangerous. One must be careful. Youth is beautiful, but one must be careful."

I saw that she wanted to make me responsible for her crime. She gesticulated and rubbed her hands nervously.

"The girl is the one who suffers," she continued. "The man enjoys himself and the girl is the one who suffers. One must be careful. After all, it is not difficult. There are ways and you know them because you are grown up. It's a matter of two lives . . ."

"Are you going to do it now?" Cecilia interrupted her bravely.

"Right now. If not now, when? The sooner the better. These things have to be taken care of in time."

Cecilia interrupted her again.

"Will I suffer much?" she asked.

The woman made a grimace that looked like a smile.

"That depends on you, my girl. If you are nervous, naturally you will suffer. This isn't easy. Besides, the police are on the lookout. And I would be the one who would have to pay. . . . You wouldn't, naturally! My children would pay for it. The boy you saw a minute ago studies engineering. If I failed him I don't know what would happen to his career. I do these things for him, but I'm tired of it. One more year and I'll retire."

Cecilia was held in a stupor. The fat woman continued.

"You two are very young. You don't know what life is. Every pleasure has its price. Love exists; you can't prevent that, but it is possible to prevent complications. If my hand slips, good-by! A good thing that I am a professional and not an ordinary amateur. There is my diploma. I tell you this to put you at ease, not out of vanity. Many people have passed through here, and I have learned to see reality without prejudices. Because of that, I advise you . . ."

Cecilia displayed great distress. It could be seen in her tense attitude, in the bitterness of her expression. When the woman moved toward the door I could see that she felt relieved. The fat woman patted her head.

"Come along, honey. This way . . ." and she gestured toward the exit.

I squeezed the hand of Gustavo's sweetheart and stammered, "Good luck, Ceci."

She looked at me sweetly. I would have liked to kiss her, but that would have been undesirable, even audacious. Before leaving, the midwife turned to me.

"Sit down and relax. The girl is in good hands." Then she added, "It wouldn't bother you if my daughter comes to study her piano lesson, would it? She has to practice."

I shrugged my shoulders. They went out and I was alone. I picked up a magazine and immediately tossed it aside. I lit a cigarette while I thought how good a cup of coffee would taste. What attitude would Gustavo adopt here? I asked myself. I tried to imagine myself among those things—cushions, curtains with faded fringes, shadows, faded odors. I wanted to impersonate myself, as a pastime, of course—but suddenly the idea struck me that Cecilia might die. My heart beat faster. A muffled sound of plates and silverware was audible in the distance. Also, some hidden voices reached me in opaque waves.

That was when the little girl came in. She was at

most fifteen years old, but she was wizened, sad, bleached, her scanty, limp hair tied behind the neck with a blue ribbon.

"Pardon," she said, and passed before me without waiting for an answer.

"Go right ahead. . . ."

She sat before the piano, opened a music book she had carried underneath her arm, and began playing a scale, a monochord, puerile melody. I concentrated on her back, since there was no escape. The girl stopped.

"Pardon my back."

"That's all right."

She went on with the scale. She was clumsy, made mistakes continually. The music—that useless, empty music —began to possess me. I thought of Cecilia. It occurred to me that it was better the child should be playing since it would keep me from hearing the screams, if any. The image of Gustavo intervened too. I saw him as inferior to me, obscure and distant. Cecilia belongs to me, I told myself. But this idea soon appeared to me as impure and mean. The notes of the piano dripped down on my head. I had the sudden impulse to pull back the curtains and let light into the room; but, out of timidity or I don't know what, I didn't dare to. I was choking. I lit another cigarette. I listened attentively to steps that dissolved into the scale, that came and went, that mounted and lurched slowly downward, like a heavy ball pushed by an imbecile. I took up the magazine again. "The Secret of Happiness Is Within Us." "Is Cancer Incurable?" "Cookies That Taste Glorious." I let it go. And I smoked again while the midwife's daughter pounded and pounded the piano. I know that I smoked a lot.

When the door opened, I had been dozing for some time. The fat woman came in and the little girl stopped her exercises.

"You can relax," she said, putting a hand on my shoulder. "Everything came out all right."

I was stupefied.

"Next time, my boy," she continued, "you must be

careful. It is better to avoid these operations. For the girl and for yourself. And also for me. . . . Go away, Charito," she told her daughter.

The little girl took down the book, closed the piano and went out silently, head down.

"You should be proud. The girl is brave."

"Where is she?" I asked.

"Resting. She'll come soon. You men think that this is very simple, but it is a bit painful. All right. If she wants to, she can go dancing tonight."

She went on talking, so that when Cecilia appeared I couldn't be as affectionate with her as I had meant to be. Right there the fat lady extended her hand to us.

"My son will see you to the door."

And so it was. Before going out, I asked the engineering student, "What's the time?"

"It's eleven-thirty," he answered.

I looked at Cecilia attentively for the first time. She was deadened, transparent, as though outside herself.

"How do you feel?"

"Not too badly. Let's take a taxi. Susan must be worried. It's very late."

I left her at her cousin's house where, according to previous agreement, she would pass the day. When I said good-by, I kissed her hand.

"Thank you, Quique. I'll never forget this favor. You are so good."

"Oh, Ceci! You don't have to thank me."

I went home and I couldn't eat a bite for lunch. There was a knot of something like nausea and shame in my throat. At two in the afternoon Gustavo came to see me.

"Thanks, pal. That was a gesture I won't forget."

He was shining. His blue suit, his silvery necktie, his white shirt, his lustrous shoes: all were impeccable. I had the impression that he considered himself purged of guilt and that all his sin had passed to me and stained me forever. I remained silent.

"How did you like the midget's piano playing?" he asked me.

"But . . . how did you know?"

"It's a trick of the old lady. She says the men hold up better that way."

"Have you been there before?"

"I've brought a lot of clients to the fat lady. You think this is the first time I've . . . ?"

"Bastard!" I yelled heatedly, gritting my teeth. It came from inside me with uncontainable frenzy.

"What? Does it bother you that I've been there before?" he asked cynically, impassively.

"Get out, coward! Get out before I break your neck."

"My, aren't we mad! It's not that serious!"

He turned his back and left. I went right to bed to cry like a baby. From envy? Repugnance? Impotence? Love? I don't know. And although when I think of Cecilia I feel all right, still, perhaps because I'm sentimental, I haven't recovered completely. When I feel a little better I'll call her and go out with her.

Octavio Paz

Born in Mexico City in 1914, Octavio Paz has published four collections of poetry in the "Tezontle" and "Cuadernos Americanos" series. The American edition of his book on life and thought in Mexico, *The Labyrinth of Solitude*, appeared in 1962.

Eve's Dream

I

She closes her eyes and within
she is naked and young, at the foot of the tree.
In its shade rest the tiger, the bull.
Three lambs of fog she gives the tiger,
three doves to the bull, blood and feathers.
No offerings of smoke desires the tiger
nor doves the bull: it is you they want.
And the doves fly, the bull flies,
and she also, naked Milky Way,
flies in a dark, visceral sky.
A malevolent dagger, cat eyes
and yellow straw mat wings
follow her through the air. And she fights
and defeats the serpent, defeats the eagle,
and above the moon's horn rises. . . .

II

Through space whirls the maiden.
Errant clouds, whirlwinds, air.
The sky is a yawning mouth,
a shark's mouth in which laugh
edged lightnings, the stars.
Lily-dressed she approaches,
and pulls the teeth of the sleeper

185

and tosses them into the ageless air:
blinking islands, the stars fell;
on the cloth fell the scattered salt,
a shower of feathers was the wounded heron,
the guitar broke and the mirror,
too, like the moon, fell in splinters.
And the statue crumbled. Virile limbs
writhed in the dust, alive.

III

Rocks and the sea. The aged sun
burns the stones which the sea turns bitter.
Sky of stone. Sea of stone. No one.
Kneeling, she digs in the sand,
claws the rock with broken nails.
Why disinter statues from the dust?
The mouth of the dead is dead.
On the carpet she gathers the figures
of her infinite jigsaw puzzle.
And always one is missing, only one,
and no one knows where, hidden.
In the parlor the visitors chat.
The wind whimpers in the shadowed garden.
It is buried at the foot of the tree. Who?
The key, the word, the ring . . .
But it is very late already, all is dark,
the visitors are leaving and her mother
tells them: "Good night, good night. . . ."

IV

At the foot of the tree again. Nothing there:
tin cans, broken bottles, a knife,
the remnants of a Sunday now rusty.
Bellows the Samson bull, wounded and alone
among the infinitudes of the night in ruins
and through the yellow fields wander
the balding lion, the faded tiger.

She leaves the deserted garden
and, by rainy streets, arrives at home.
She knocks, but no one answers; she enters
and there is nobody behind each door,
and she goes from nobody to door until she arrives
at the last door, the walled one,
the one her father shut each night.
She looks for the key, but it is lost;
she knocks, she scratches, she pounds it.
During centuries she pounds it,
and the door grows higher each century
and more closed and more solid with each blow.
She cannot reach it now and only waits,
seated in her little chair, for someone to open it;
she is an old woman now, as old
as the dust that sleeps in the corners:
Lord, open the doors of your cloud,
open your badly healed wounds,
rain upon my wrinkled breasts,
rain upon the bones and the rocks,
may your seed break the shell,
the crust of my hardened blood.
Return me to the night of the Beginning,
to be torn from your side,
dark planet that your light kindles.

Sueño de Eva

I

Ella cierra los ojos y en su adentro
está desnuda y niña, al pie del árbol.
Reposan a su sombra el tigre, el toro.
Tres corderos de bruma le da al tigre,
tres palomas al toro, sangre y plumas.
Ni plegarias de humo quiere el tigre
ni palomas el toro: a ti te quieren.
Y vuelan las palomas, vuela el toro,

y ella también, desnuda vía láctea,
vuela en un cielo visceral, oscuro.
Un maligno puñal ojos de gato
y amarillentas alas de petate
la sigue entre los aires. Y ella lucha
y vence a la serpiente, vence al águila,
y sobre el cuerno de la luna asciende . . .

II

Por los espacios gira la doncella.
Nubes errantes, torbellinos, aire.
El cielo es una boca que bosteza,
boca de tiburón en donde ríen,
afilados relámpagos, los astros.
Vestida de azucena ella se acerca
y le arranca los dientes al dormido
y al aire sin edades los arroja:
islas que parpadean cayeron las estrellas,
cayó al mantel la sal desparramada,
lluvia de plumas fué la garza herida,
se quebró la guitarra y el espejo
también, como la luna, cayó en trizas.
Y la estatua cayó. Viriles miembros
se retorcieron en el polvo, vivos.

III

Rocas y mar. El sol envejecido
quema las piedras que la mar amarga.
Cielo de piedra. Mar de piedra. Nadie.
Arrodillada cava las arenas,
cava la piedra con las uñas rotas.
¿A qué desenterrar del polvo estatuas?
La boca de los muertos está muerta.
Sobre la alfombra junta las figuras
de su rompecabezas infinito.
Y siempre falta una, sólo una,

y nadie sabe dónde está, secreta.
En la sala platican las visitas.
El viento gime en el jardín en sombras.
Está enterrada al pie del árbol. ¿Quién?
La llave, la palabra, la sortija . . .
Pero es muy tarde ya, todo está oscuro,
se marchan las visitas y su madre
las dice: buenas noches, buenas noches . . .

IV

Al pie del árbol otra vez. No hay nada:
latas, botellas rotas, un cuchillo,
los restos de un domingo ya oxidado.
Muge el toro sansón, herido y solo
por los sinfines de la noche en ruinas
y por los prados amarillos rondan
el león calvo, el tigre despintado.
Ella se aleja del jardín desierto
y por calles lluviosas llega a casa.
Llama, mas nadie le contesta; avanza
y no hay nadie detrás de cada puerta
y va de nadie a puerta hasta que llega
a la última puerta, la tapiada,
la que el padre cerraba cada noche.
Busca la llave pero se ha perdido,
la golpea, la araña, la golpea,
durante siglos la golpea
y la puerta es más alta a cada siglo
y más cerrada y puerta a cada golpe.
Ella ya no la alcanza y sólo aguarda,
sentada en su sillita, que alguien abra;
es una vieja ya tan retevieja
como el polvo que duerme en los rincones:
señor, abre las puertas de tu nube,
abre tus cicatrices mal cerradas,
llueve sobre mis senos arrugados,
llueve sobre los huesos y las piedras,

que tu semilla rompa la corteza,
la costra de mi sangre endurecida.
Devuélveme a la noche del Principio,
de tu costado desprendida sea
planeta opaco que tu luz enciende.

EDUARDO ANGUITA

At one time honory Chilean Consul to Mexico, Anguita was born in the city of Linares in 1914. He studied law and the humanities at Chile's Catholic University, and the Catholic influence has strongly colored his work. A literary disciple of Vicente Huidobro, he is the author of two volumes of poetry and two verse anthologies.

The True Countenance

I have looked upon a savagely potent countenance
of soft lines, of diverse directions.
I have confronted it until it dissolved like cloud,
and saw, behind, the true Countenance with no beginning
     or end.
It was the faceless countenance, empty,
but it gazed, with what? Empty,
earless, but it listened, with what? Empty,
noseless, but it apprehended, with what? Maskless,
pulseless, lifeless, but stern, severe.
It was a mask true and invisible
raised above the body on this summer afternoon.

Behind the person is a countenance made of order,
a countenance similar to the flash of a sword.
Can one be without being something? Like the presence
     rising
from a grove between the sky and the leaves, the little girl
     I watched
half-opened her face to the breeze and displayed the Aspect.

Most beneficent day for my understanding and madness
that frees me tranquilly from love and pain:
unite in me your broad palms of light and your dark time
that the squandered instants and the true lights that occur
invest the moment of my unique countenance.

Thus must I kiss thee some day, woman whose counte-
    nance I separate like waters,
as I separate your lips, unveil your eyes until I see you well.
Love is no longer possible, nor life. As in the bottom of a
    dry pond,
in your depths will remain affixed, like bones or an in-
    scription,
the time that is my aureole, my niche: faithful time!

El verdadero rostro

He mirado un rostro ferozmente potente,
De rasgos suaves, de diversas direcciones.
Lo he enrostrado hasta hacerlo caer como nube,
Y vi, atrás, el verdadero Rostro sin delante ni detrás.
Era el rostro sin cara, vacío,
Pero que miraba, ¿por dónde? Vacío,
Sin oídos, pero que escuchaba, ¿por dónde? Vacío,
Sin nariz, pero que presentía, ¿por dónde? Sin máscara,
Sin palpitación, sin vida, pero muy severo.
Era una máscara tan verdadera e invisible
Erguida sobre el tronco en esta tarde de verano.

Detrás de la persona hay un rostro hecho de orden,
Un rostro semejante al brillo de la espada.
¿Se puede ser sin ser algo? Como la presencia que tras-
    ciende
De las arboledas, entre el cielo y las hojas, la pequeña niña
    observada
Entreabría su cara a unas ráfagas y mostraba el Aspecto.

Día muy benéfico a mi entendimiento y locura,
Que con tanto reposo me libras del amor y el dolor:
Junta en mí tus anchas palmas de luz a tu tiempo oscuro,
Y los instantes desperdiciados y las verdaderas luces que
    ocurren
Instalen el momento de mi único Rostro.

Así he de besarte algún día, mujer cuyo rostro separo como
      aguas,
Como separo tus labios y despejo tus ojos hasta verte bien.
Ya el amor no es posible, ni la vida. Como en fondo de
      estanque seco,
En tu fondo quedará pegado, semejante a huesos o in-
      scripción,
El tiempo que es mi aureola, mi nicho: ¡tiempo fiel!

HUGO LINDO

Born in La Union, El Salvador, in 1917, Hugo Lindo's published work includes three volumes of poetry, two short story collections and a novel.

Sleeping in the Salt

Nobody said, "Create the water,"
because it already was.

It was sleeping in the salt,
limpid and quiet.
It was dwelling in Chaos
and the Word was dwelling in it.

Life water! Mother water!
Ancient water!

The spores of the future—
the river, the sea, the storm,
the leaves of tin and glass
that colonize iodine,
the trees of coral,
the submarine stars,
the naked goddess-fish—
were also in it.

Life water! Mother water!
Ancient water!

Impregnated with silence
the secret Voice waited.

Nobody said, "Create the water,"
because it already was.

And in it the vessel of God
voyaging toward complex life:

that of the bird in the cloud,
that of the tree on the mountain,
that of the deer,
that of the wild beast,
that of man with his torch
and with his blind ash . . .
In the water, life mother,
ancient life,
new mother!

Nobody said, "Create the water."
And there my presence was
even before the voice
from earth's crags
should seek a channel to the Word
through the poem.

It was sleeping in the salt,
limpid and quiet,
seedbed of the centuries
and itself timeless: eternal water!

Dormida en la sal

Nadie dijo "hágase el agua",
porque ya era.

Era dormida en la sal,
clara y quieta.
Ella anidaba en el Caos
y el Verbo anidaba en ella.

¡Agua vida, agua madre,
agua vieja!

Las esporas del futuro
—el río, el mar, la tormenta,
las hojas de estaño y vidrio
que el yodo pueblan,

los árboles de coral,
las submarinas estrellas,
las desnudas diosas-peces—
también en ella.

¡Agua vida, agua madre,
agua vieja!

Impregnada de silencio
guardaba la Voz secreta.

Nadie dijo "hágase el agua",
porque ya era.

Y en ella el barco de Dios
rumbo a la vida compleja:
la del pájaro en la nube,
la del árbol en la sierra,
la del venado,
la de la fiera,
la del hombre con su antorcha
y con su ceniza ciega . . .
¡En el agua, vida madre,
vida vieja,
madre nueva!

Nadie dijo "hágase el agua",
y ahí estaba mi presencia
desde antes de que la voz
en los riscos de la tierra,
buscase cauce hacia el Verbo
por el poema.

Era dormida en la sal,
clara y quieta.
¡Semillero de los siglos
y ella sin tiempo: agua eterna!

IDA GRAMCKO

Five published volumes of poetry have come from the pen of this young writer, who was born in 1925 in the seaport town of Puerto Cabello, some seventy miles from Caracas.

Dream

Take heed, whoever said
he finds happiness and peace
in a beatific and tranquil dream;
take note of what I say and what I believe.
Know you, nocturnal friend,
what thing it really is that we call dream?
Take heed, my brother,
without sorrow and without misgiving.
I, who have dreamed, I, who have not slept,
ask you voicelessly from my couch:
Do you believe a dream protects from the abyss,
rescues from attack and fire?
I, immobile dreamer, have not believed
in my peaceful countenance when I sleep.
I struggle, dreaming sordidly with myself,
with a strange bird, with the wind,
with a sharp and pointed peak
that pierces my temples and my brain
and I leave blood on the cushion and
my wounded locks float blazing, shrieking.
Dreamer and sleepwalker are the same.
One wanders amid fog, an orphan.
Who stitched the pillows? Forgetfulness?
The unsteady hand of memory
with a somber clue
wove the cocoon of fabric
with a long serpent of linen

that entwines the soul and the body.
Beware of him who once told me
to find seraphic calm in dreams;
beware of my belief, of my question,
which is that of every wakened dreamer.
I believe in my heart, its hidden flame
beneath the sheets, burning.
I believe in my mute blood
flowing like a river of the inferno.
Does anyone believe in the quiet of the tomb,
in the peace of the dead?
They want to believe . . . they have never believed.
Rest in peace, it is only a great desire;
rest in peace, but peace does not listen;
rest in peace, but rest is blind.
Death, sleepless, looks towards the struggle
and the dream, most intimate vigil.

Sueño

Atienda aquel que dijo
hallar dicha y sosiego
en un sueño beatífico y tranquilo;
atienda a lo que digo y lo que creo.
¿ Sabes, nocturno amigo,
a qué cosa en verdad llamamos sueño?
Atiende, hermano mío,
sin pena y sin recelo,
yo, que he soñado, yo, que no he dormido,
te pregunto sin voz desde mi lecho:
¿ Crees que el sueño protege del abismo,
rescata del asalto y del incendio?
Yo, soñadora inmóvil, no he creído
en mi rostro apacible cuando duermo.
Lucho soñando, sórdida, conmigo,
con un pájaro extraño, con el viento,
con un agudo y afilado pico

que me horada las sienes y el cerebro
y dejo sangre en el cojín y heridos
flotan ardiendo, aullando, mis cabellos.
Soñador y sonámbulo es lo mismo.
Se va entre nieblas, huérfano.
¿Quién hiló las almohadas? ¿El olvido?
La mano movediza del recuerdo
con un sombrío ovillo
y tejió la crisálida del lienzo
con una larga víbora de lino
que se enrosca en el alma y en el cuerpo.
Atienda aquel que alguna vez me dijo
hallar quietud seráfica en el sueño;
atienda a mi creencia, a mi pregunta,
que es la de todo soñador despierto.
Creo en mi corazón, su llama oculta
bajo las sábanas, ardiendo.
Creo en mi sangre muda
corriendo como un río del infierno.
¿Cree alguien en la calma de las tumbas,
en la paz de los muertos?
Quieren creer . . . ¡No lo han creído nunca!
Descansa en paz, sólo es un gran deseo.
Descansa en paz, pero la paz no escucha;
descansa en paz, pero el descanso es ciego.
La muerte, insomne, mira hacia la lucha
y el sueño es el más íntimo desvelo.

JOSE DONOSO

Born in Santiago in 1928, this young author of two collections of short stories was awarded a Doherty Foundation scholarship in 1949, and attended the universities of Chile and Princeton. The following story is set in the barren, windswept reaches of southern Chile, near the Strait of Magellan.

Denmarker

That evening after work Don Gaspar, the accountant, announced that he was thirsty. I allowed myself to be convinced easily because, in the isolation of a Magellan ranch, any pretext to break the monotony is a blessing, even though the pretext itself has become habitual. Don Gaspar and I were accustomed to going to the Denmarker's Post on Saturdays and Sundays, but then the thirst was so routine that we did not even need that excuse for going. Saturdays and Sundays there were often as many as thirty or forty horses tied to the hitching rail of the Post, and in the half-light of the interior, full of smoke, tumult and quarrels, Doña Concepción and Licha silently replaced the empty bottles and burnt candles on the tables. But, in addition to the weekends, Don Gaspar felt thirsty from time to time on a workday too, and this certainly could be considered an exceptional circumstance. This time, besides thirst, each of us had another reason: I was leaving for good within the week and had come to say good-by; Don Gaspar wanted to congratulate Licha on her coming marriage.

It was five o'clock. We saddled up and went off at a gallop along the trail that led to the Denmarker's. We would have light until we arrived, because in summer darkness does not come until about ten. This was the last time I would be making the trip, and I wanted to look at everything carefully, in order to remember it later, in distant days and places. But it was not necessary to look. We seemed to remain motionless, so monotonous was the landscape—if you can call it that, this smooth emptiness of plain, this sphere in whose cold and windy center we remained in spite of our horses' galloping. Only the sky changed. Clouds passed by, casting pools of shadow that floated or retreated, carried by the wind, while the sun slowly followed its course across the immense warp of the sky.

Suddenly a dark stain appeared on the horizon. To catch sight of it far away—as if it were falling off the edge of the planet and then growing larger—placed us once again within time and measurable distance. Then, on seeing it resolve itself into the small cube of corrugated iron that was the Post, erupting abruptly in the center of the bald plain, something vibrated inside us: contentment, peace, the certainty that there at last warmth and wine awaited us—and people, different ones from those we worked with every day. Besides, there were two women: Doña Concepción, fat and smiling mistress of the Post, and her daughter, Licha, thin as a shadow.

Because it was a weekday, we found no more than half a dozen horses at the rail. We tied ours next to the others. Looking at the reddish smudge that girded the western horizon, to calculate how long it would be possible for us to remain at the Post, I warmed my numbed hands against my mare's steaming nostrils.

Doña Concepción came out to welcome us with demonstrations of surprise and joy. One could always count on her amiable words and good humor. Of course, she had her daughter and she had her own Post, which must have made good money. She charged such exorbitant prices for everything that it was not uncommon to spend years trying to work out of the debts contracted there. However, I think we went to the Denmarker's more to be near her than for anything else. She was virtually the only woman in the district —Licha didn't count—and despite her years and her bulk, she reminded us of an entirely different, pleasant world. She always wore black because she was a widow. Her puffy, powdered face often became disfigured with guffaws so violent that all the excess, soft flesh took some minutes to regain equilibrium about the heavily made-up eyes, the fleshy, pallid lips, the diminutive nose. She led us to a table next to the stove, calling Licha to attend to us. The girl did so without warmth or enthusiasm.

Doña Concepción became upset on hearing that I had come to say good-by.

"How lonely I am going to be!" she cried, smiling.

Her hand had an unusual tremor when she placed the glasses on the table, and I noticed that her dark hair was strangely disordered. I looked at Don Gaspar to see if he had noticed, but the little old man turned his eyes away as if he were ashamed. On gulping the first drink, he made a noise in his sinewy throat, tanned by wine and wind.

"How lonely I am going to be," Doña Concepción repeated more quietly.

I thought she was also referring to the marriage of her daughter, who, I had heard, was leaving the following morning to get married in Punta Arenas. Then she stood up and her huge mass disappeared through the kitchen door with an unsteady step.

"Doña Concepción seems a little strange today," I ventured.

Don Gaspar did not answer. He had a curious way of drinking. He held his small body very stiffly in the chair, his hairy, heavy hands grasping the edge of the table without letting go, except to fill the glass and carry it to his mouth. But now he was crumpled in the seat and his fingers had not decided on a stable position. After a while he mumbled, "It's just that Licha is going, and it's very lonely here. . . ."

Actually there were very few people in the Post that night. At one table three men played cards silently around a candle. At another a man tilted his chair back against the wall, drank a little, hummed a little, and from time to time looked at the corpse of flat light that remained in the windows, or seemed to cock an ear to the wind that, after hurling itself along the plain, divided itself, whistling against the angles of the house.

"We should congratulate the gringo, Stirling," I suggested. "Look, there he goes. . . ."

Don Gaspar looked in the direction I had indicated, shrugging when he saw the long, hunched figure of the Scotsman wandering among the tables, following Licha. She was crying when she brought the bottle we had ordered.

"What's wrong, girl?" Don Gaspar asked.

"Nothing. Another sty, that's all," was her answer.

She scarcely had a face. Pug-nosed and pale, everything about her was niggardly—her eyes, her nose, her thin mouth. Her sparse hair hung lankly.

At the moment Licha was about to withdraw, Don Gaspar took her by the wrist. She stood frozen, staring at him. Then she burst out crying. The gringo, Stirling, came limping up and took her by the shoulders.

"She told him out of pure envy," the girl exclaimed. "Just so I wouldn't get married. But I'm going to get married anyway. I bet that even you have slept with the old pig. . . ."

"But Licha, what does it matter?" the gringo said in his half-speech. "I knew all that before you were born. . . ."

Licha dried her eyes with the edge of her skirt and, still sniffling, went to wait on another table, followed closely by the gringo.

"What had to happen has happened," the accountant murmured.

"But why so many tears and insults? You'd think she was dying."

"It's because Concepción hasn't resigned herself. You get ferocious here when you're going to be left alone."

"But what's going on? I've never seen Licha this way, much less Doña Concepción. They should be happy to have caught the gringo, who, in addition to everything else, is going to be an overseer. I don't understand. . . ."

"Of course, you don't understand! I, who have been here so many years, don't understand. So how can you? Concepción, for example, I don't know her. And I met her two years after I came to this ranch from up North, more than thirty years ago.

"I was a grown man when I arrived from Chiloé to try my luck, to work for a couple of years in order to go back to my land with my pockets full. But, like so many others, I stayed on and on, and I'm still here.

"It was hard to get acclimated at the beginning, to accept so much loneliness, so much cold, so much work to earn a few pesos that couldn't buy anything here . . . and which couldn't be saved either. Besides, and this was the worst part, an accountant has no right to treat the owner or the overseer as an equal, nor can he do the same with the shepherds. I was desperate; I wanted to go back North, wanted to be any place but here.

"But one fine Sunday I let myself be dragged along to this Post to have a few drinks and forget my troubles. At that time the owner was a Denmarker, a man of about my own age and situation, who knew the whole world because he had been a sailor. He lived alone. Like me, he was a great one for talking and drinking, and by talking and talking and drinking and drinking we became close friends. From then on my life changed, because I spent all my free time here. Besides, I opened an account. I think one of the reasons I never went back North is that I have never been able to finish paying it.

"It was funny to see us together, the Denmarker and me, because I, like a good *Chilote*, have always been short and dark. But you should have seen what a chunk of man he was! Immense and blond, standing on the bare plain, he cast a shadow in the afternoon that was endless. He had uncommon strength—which he demonstrated once and for all when he first arrived by smashing in a drunk's face—and a voice that seemed as though it would burst this tin box. Everyone was afraid of him, especially when he got mad, which didn't happen often. Then he would give orders in a strange tongue that nobody understood; and since they didn't understand, they didn't know what to do; and the gringo would get madder and madder until he ended up by drawing a gun. But he was a jolly Denmarker and as lacking in malice as a child. So, in spite of fearing him, everybody liked him. He gave good service; nothing was ever lacking in the Post. Besides, he knew how to cook some strange, very tasty dishes. Since he was a bit tight-fisted, he never went to town, which was a day's journey then because of the bad roads.

"One summer afternoon when our friendship was about two years old, I noticed he was acting strangely. It was a Sunday, so there were a great many people in the Post. But he wasn't waiting on tables; he had paid three boys to do the work he usually did by himself. He was combed and had put on a stiff collar and a tie. He walked from one room to the other restlessly, doing nothing, looking, talking a minute with one person and then another. When it was already growing late, he looked at his pocket watch and suggested to me that we go sit on the rail and smoke for a while. All this was unheard of, including the extreme tidiness of the rooms at the Post—which was like a small hotel —but I asked no questions. Instead, I talked of other things while the quiet gringo kept an alert, blue-eyed gaze fixed on the plain.

" 'There they come,' he exclaimed at last, his face lighting up.

" 'Who?' I asked.

"He pointed to a speck on the horizon. Little by little, as it drew near, we realized that it was an automobile. I repeated my question but he refused to satisfy me until the vehicle stopped in front of the Post and five women got out.

"At that time, when the town was so remote, these caravans of women frequently traveled about the ranches, lodging in the independent posts. Most of them were old and ugly; but for us, who in many cases had not seen a woman for years, everything about them was marvelous. We were thirsty and the oasis was here. Although a bit muddy, it was at least real water. They would usually stay two or three days. Then they would return to town with all our money, but considerably more bedraggled than when they arrived.

"Hearing women's voices, the sheepherders in the Post rushed out to welcome them. They didn't flinch on seeing the thirty or forty men, stinking of wine, unshaven, anxious to possess them instantly. Of those who had come, four were the ordinary merchandise in this type of business. However, the fifth was a big brunette, with a wide face and mobile, padded hips. She seemed to us the acme of desirability.

"We all wanted the brunette, but the Denmarker had staked out a prior claim. Impatiently we knocked at the door of the gringo's room. At last he came out, very seriously and well-combed, locking the door with a key. He said that only he was going to take care of the brunette.

"There was a terrible disorder during those days the women spent at the Post. The news had spread like wildfire through the district, and people kept coming and coming. The sheepherders discussed them, giving data and recommendations to those who had not yet seen them. There were fifty, a hundred, sheepherders in the Post, quarreling to be first, getting drunk, stealing wine, breaking windows and glasses. But a great, smiling serenity had fallen over the Denmarker. Nothing of what was happening around touched him. A few of his bellows would re-establish a momentary order.

"As the days went by I grew drunker and drunker until, by the third night, I was completely stupefied. The others seemed to have forgotten the brunette, but I hadn't. I was savagely enraged at the Denmarker, but he only smiled at my insults and then went to wait on someone who called him.

"I convinced one of the sheepherders, who was as drunk as I, that the situation was unbearable. We went out of the Post, led a horse around to the high window of the room where the brunette was lodged, and in the darkness I managed to reach the window sill. I broke the windowpane with my fist and let myself fall onto the bed where the woman was sleeping. My friend fell in behind me. While we struggled with the screaming woman, the kerosene lamp turned over, setting the sheets and bedclothes afire. Outside there was a great uproar and shouting. The Denmarker came running in, followed by a number of sheepherders. They overflowed the room, which was illuminated only by the burning bed where we were still fighting over the woman. They brought buckets of water to put out the flames, and also to separate us, as one separates two fighting dogs.

"As I was unconscious, they must have tossed me in a corner to sleep. The next day I awoke early. The sheepherders had left or were preparing to do so. The women were already in the automobile. The Denmarker dressed elegantly, packed his suitcase, locked up the Post, and left in the automobile with the women.

"He returned the following week accompanied by the brunette. They had been married in Punta Arenas. She— Doña Concepción, as she has been called since then—took charge of the Post along with her husband. At first we made bets as to who would be the first to get on familiar terms with her, but one threat from her to call her husband was enough to blast any pretensions.

"I was in love, in love. I bothered her all the time, boldly, but it was as though she didn't see me. I fought every day with the Denmarker, who had already threatened to deny me entrance and to take me to court for the year's bill I owed him.

"One night I found Concepción alone outside the Post. I drew near, prepared to take her by force right there, but she rejected me.

" 'Why are you trying to play the saint?' I asked.

"She struck me across the mouth and screamed that if I touched her she would call her husband to kick me apart. Humiliated, I turned away to go back to the Post. But in the darkness her voice stopped me.

" 'Gaspar, don't be like that with me. . . .' "

"It was the most immense night I have ever seen. Her eyes, heavy with Rimmel, shone steadily in the darkness. In that moment something of the truth about all our lives struck my consciousness, and something—I don't know what— broke inside of me.

"I ran to the Post and entered.

" 'Denmarker, Denmarker, come and have a drink with me, you disgusting gringo!' I shouted.

"It must have been funny to see the embrace I gave him, he so big and I so small. In any case, I think he understood something of what it was all about because I never saw him smile like that time. I swear that I have never in all my life felt a stronger bond with a human being than I felt that night with the Denmarker.

"Little by little in the district they began to forget Concepción's past. The Post was never more agreeable than during that time—always clean, never lacking something good to eat or well-made beds in which to pass the night if drunkenness or snow kept us from returning. The gringo didn't drink as much as before because his wife told him, 'The smell of drunks in my room brings back bad memories. . . .'

"And faced with her threat of not letting him in, he abstained.

"Concepción was a model wife and, for me, a real friend. Years later, I married. My wife, very dignified and Catholic, became great friends with her. I never told how the Denmarker's wife arrived here, and Concepción has been grateful to me for that until this day because, since my wife was educated and from a good family, her friendship was a source of great pride to Concepción. After five years Licha was born, and in ten years the gringo died from some disease."

We remained for a long time without speaking. All the silence of the plain seemed to have moved inside the Post. The three men went on playing cards and the one who had been drinking alone was asleep in his corner. Only Licha came and went among the tables, taking away a bottle, cleaning a smear of mud on the floor, bringing dishes of cauliflower soup. Then Doña Concepción approached us, staggering a little. Don Gaspar helped her to sit down.

"How lonely I am going to be. . . ." she sighed.

We did not answer.

"You are going," she said, looking at me with the same bright eyes, heavy with Rimmel, that Don Gaspar had seen that night. "And Licha is leaving me tomorrow for Punta Arenas to marry the gringo, Stirling. . . ."

"Didn't they say she was going with someone else?" I asked, to make conversation.

"Ah, that's finished. I don't know what's the matter with

that girl. She isn't interested in love. It's strange. All she wants is to leave here, nothing else. The gringo is going as overseer for the Suarez, a small ranch near Punta Arenas. They say it has beautiful houses. . . ."

She took a sip and asked, "You know the gringo, Stirling, don't you?"

"Not very well," I answered.

"He's that skinny one that was here a while ago, the one that doesn't even laugh when he's drunk. The only thing he likes is to go fishing in the canals here. He's been coming around for a long time, but he's so ugly and so old. How was I to know he was courting the girl? But these gringos are toads. How is one to know what they are thinking when they spend hours and hours alone, fishing?"

She took another sip. Don Gaspar made a gesture to stop her, but she cut the movement short.

"I don't deny it will be good for her to get married," she went on. "The gringo has money and Licha will become the wife of an administrator, which is what she wants. But, you know, Gaspar? That gringo makes me sick—those thin hands, cold all the time, that limping and limping. She makes me sick too. You'll think I'm dumb, but I would have preferred her to marry that crazy Marin who was chasing after her, drunken and quarrelsome as he was. But she, the fool, wanted nothing to do with him and afterward the cowboy went North. What's become of him now? He was so high-spirited. Remember the voice he had? Yes, sir, sounded like thunder. Made you scared here, in the belly, like the voice of the poor Denmarker, may he rest in peace. . . ."

She went on talking for a long time, complaining about her daughter, about the gringo, remembering, until her voice grew fuzzy and her words more and more incoherent. Then she crossed her arms on the table and went to sleep with her head resting on them.

The gringo, Stirling, approached. Lightly resting one hand on Doña Concepción's head, he said very slowly, as if afraid of awakening her, "Poor thing, she's drunk. . . . I'll call Licha."

Licha woke her mother and told the gringo to take her

to the room, that she'd be there in a minute. As she wiped
the table, she said without raising her eyes, "I'm going to
get married anyway, so she'll see, just so she'll be left all
alone, that's all. . . ."

"But the gringo already knew," Don Gaspar exclaimed
with a disheartened voice.

She raised her reddened eyes and fixed them on the old
man.

"How can you understand? Don't you see that things
can never be the same anymore?"

It was time to leave. We wished Licha happiness. She
did not appear to be moved. We mounted and turned
around to say good-by to the girl, who had accompanied us
to the door.

It was a wide, open night. The wind whipped by, seeking in the emptiness of the plain something in which to en-
tangle itself while it swept the starry sky. In a little while
the mass and then the lights of the Denmarker's Post disappeared. Because the wind was strong and there was ice
underfoot, we preferred not to gallop. We rode silently for
long hours, knowing we would not arrive at the ranch until
daybreak.

Somewhere along the road, I heard Don Gaspar mutter
to himself in the darkness.

"I've never seen her drunk . . ."

It was as though everything, even the best and most
beautiful, had ended forever.

Maria Elena Walsh

Born in the province of Buenos Aires in 1930, this young Argentine poet is the author of four published volumes of verse.

The Forest of Agonies

I come from the hands of God,
I am of love and of the earth.
Soon the days will gather me in
with a flower in my hair,
stretched out beneath the autumn sky,
dead of love, of life, of sadness.

I come from an enveloping night
like the womb that held me:
I bring its form of silence,
its starless distances,
for I am born each dawn,
with the insistent bird that wakes me.

I had eyes and tears when
they saw me for the first time,
and when they touched me I had
a home of real flesh,
and he who arrived with love gave me
a soul of tenderness and violence.

Perfumes that made one suffer,
and music that made one sad,
the lengthy taste of colors
and superficial essences,
came to me like small children,
and my whole body escaped with them.

May God say if I knew how to love him
in the children of his beauty,

may the dead gardens say
whether I was not their springtime,
may they return to me in garrulous memory
what my tongue knew not how to eternalize.

I come from the eyes of the Angel,
I am of his absence and his presence.
His tenderness is like a river
that surrounds and sustains me,
that comes to me from a graceful fountain
and with its voice makes me tremble, and trembles.

I am his beloved and I owe him
sorrow and strength.
This divine flower of loving each other
arises from eternal roots,
and an infinity is born each day
from its stem with the fragrance of purity.

I come from each act of charity,
I am of those beings who find in me
a mysterious sympathy,
and they illumine and carry me
to feel in their souls what I feel,
with another recognized and new light.

I am of the word that hurts
in a blood of tragedy,
and of its breath that falls
like ashes or like sand,
I am of solitude that invents voices
which one can never really hear.

I live in a forest of agonies,
in the atmosphere of adolescence.
Lightning flashes give me sweetness,
doves bring me war,
a branchery of music covers that
complete sky which thirst awaits.

May deep water care for me
and its transparency assist me.

I go naked, and my wealth
is in the things I do not have.
May fire transfix me and raise me
to the hard air where all burns.

I come from the hands of God,
I am of love and of the earth.
Soon the days will gather me in
with a flower in my hair,
stretched out beneath the autumn sky,
dead of love, of life, of sadness.

El bosque de agonias

Vengo de las manos de Dios,
soy del amor y de la tierra.
Ya me recogerán los días
con una flor en la cabeza,
tumbada bajo el cielo del otoño,
muerta de amor, de vida, de tristeza.

Vengo de una noche cerrada
como el vientre que me tuviera:
traigo su forma de silencio,
su lejanía sin estrellas,
por eso nazco cada amanecer,
con el pájaro fiel que me despierta.

Tuve ojos y lágrimas cuando
me miraron por vez primera,
y cundo me tocaron tuve
casa de carne verdadera,
y el que llegó con el amor me puso
un alma de ternura y de violencia.

Perfumes que hacían sufrir,
y músicas que deban pena,
largo sabor de los colores
y superficiales esencias,

a mí vinieron como criaturas,
y todo el cuerpo se me fué con ellas.

Que Dios diga si supe amarlo
en los hijos de su belleza,
que digan los jardines muertos
si yo no fuí su primavera,
que me devuelvan en locuaz memoria
lo que no supo eternizar mi lengua.

Vengo de los ojos del Angel,
soy de su ausencia y su presencia.
Es su ternura como un río
que me rodea y me sustenta,
que viene a mí desde agraciada fuente
y con su voz me hace temblar, y tiembla.

Soy su enamorada y le debo
el dolor y la fortaleza.
Esta divina flor de amarnos
sube de raices eternas,
y un infinito nace cada día
de su tallo en olores de pureza.

Vengo de toda caridad,
soy de los seres que me encuentran
en misteriosa simpatía,
y me iluminan y me llevan
a sentir en sus almas lo que siento,
con otra luz reconocida y nueva.

Soy de la palabra que duele
en una sangre de tragedia,
y de su aliento que decae
como la ceniza o la arena,
soy de la soledad que inventa voces
que nunca se podrán oír de veras.

Vivo en un bosque de agonías,
al aire de la adolescencia.
Relámpagos me dan dulzura,
palomas me traen la guerra,

ramajes musicales tapan ese
cielo completo que la sed espera.

Que el agua profunda me cuide,
y me asista su transparencia.
Vaya desnuda, y mi caudal
sean las cosas que no tengo.
Que el fuego me traspase y me levante
al aire duro donde todo quema.

Vengo de las manos de Dios,
soy del amor y de la tierra,
ya me recogerán los días
con una fior en la cabeza,
tumbada bajo el cielo del otoño,
muerta de amor, de vida, de tristeza.

Nicanor Parra

By vocation a professor of mathematics and physics at the University of Chile, and by avocation a poet, Nicanor Parra is the author of three volumes of verse. He was born in Chillán in 1914, and has traveled and studied in the United States and England.

Soliloquy of the Individual

I am the Individual.
First, I lived in a rock.
(There I carved certain figures.)
Then I sought a more appropriate place.
I am the Individual.
First, I had to obtain food,
hunt fish, birds, search for wood.
(Later I shall worry about other things.)
Make a fire;
wood, wood, where to find a piece of wood,
a bit of wood to build a fire?
I am the Individual.
At the same time I questioned myself,
beside an abyss filled with air;
a voice answered me:
I am the Individual.
Then I tried to move to another rock.
There too I carved figures.
I carved a river, buffalo,
I am the Individual.
But no. The things I did bored me,
the fire bothered me,
I wanted to see more,
I am the Individual.
I went down to a valley watered by a river,
there I found what I needed,
I found a savage people,

a tribe,
I am the Individual.
I saw that they made some things there,
they carved figures in the rocks,
they made fire, they too made fire!
I am the Individual.
They asked where I came from.
I answered, yes, that I had no fixed plans,
I answered, no, that from then on.
All right.
Then I took a bit of rock I found in a river
and began to work with it,
I began to polish it,
made of it a part of my own life.
But this is too long.
I cut some trees to float on,
I looked for fish,
I looked for different things
(I am the Individual).
Until I grew bored again.
Tempests are boring,
thunder and lightning,
I am the Individual.
All right. I began to think a little.
Inane questions came to my mind,
false problems.
Then I began wandering through some woods.
I came to one tree and then another,
I arrived at a spring,
a hole where there were rats:
Here I come, I said then,
Have you seen a tribe around here,
a savage people that makes fire?
In this manner I moved westward
accompanied by others,
or, more likely, alone.
In order to see you must believe, they told me,
I am the Individual.
I saw forms in the darkness,

clouds perhaps,
perhaps I saw clouds, I saw lightning,
all this had taken a good many days,
I felt myself dying;
I invented machines,
I made clocks,
weapons, vehicles,
I am the Individual.
I scarcely had time to bury my dead,
I scarcely had time to plant crops,
I am the Individual.
Years later I conceived certain things,
certain forms,
I crossed frontiers
and remained fixed in a sort of niche,
in a boat that sailed forty days,
forty nights,
I am the Individual.
Then came droughts,
wars came,
Colored folk entered the valley,
but I had to keep moving forward,
I had to produce.
I produced science, immutable truths,
I produced figurines,
I gave birth to books with thousand of pages,
my face grew swollen,
I built a phonograph,
the sewing machine,
the first automobiles began to appear,
I am the Individual.
Someone segregated planets,
segregated trees!
But I segregated tools,
furniture, office implements,
I am the Individual.
Cities were built also,
highways,
religious institutions passed out of fashion,

they sought joy, they sought happiness,
I am the Individual.
Later I spent my time traveling,
practicing, practicing languages,
languages,
I am the Individual.
I looked through a keyhole,
yes, I looked, I tell you, I looked,
to clear away doubts I looked
behind some curtains,
I am the Individual.
All right.
Perhaps it is better to go back to that valley,
to that rock that served me as home,
and begin to carve again,
from backward to forward, carve
the world in reverse.
But no: life has no meaning.

Soliloquio del individuo

Yo soy el Individuo.
Primero viví en una roca.
(Allí grabé algunas figuras.)
Luego busqué un lugar más apropiado.
Yo soy el Individuo.
Primero tuve que procurarme alimentos,
Buscar peces, pájaros, buscar leña.
(Ya me preocuparía de los demás asuntos.)
Hacer una fogata;
Leña, leña ¿dónde encontrar un poco de leña,
Algo de leña para hacer una fogata?
Yo soy el Individuo.
Al mismo tiempo me pregunté,
Fui a un abismo lleno de aire;
Me respondió una voz:
Yo soy el Individuo.

Después traté de cambiarme a otra roca.
Allí también grabé figuras,
Grabé un río, búfalos,
Yo soy el Individuo.
Pero no. Me aburrí de las cosas que hacía,
El fuego me molestaba,
Quería ver más,
Yo soy el Individuo.
Bajé a un valle regado por un río,
Allí encontré lo que necesitaba,
Encontré un pueblo salvaje,
Una tribu,
Yo soy el Individuo.
Vi que allí se hacían algunas cosas,
Figuras grababan en las rocas,
Hacían fuego, ¡también hacían fuego!
Yo soy el Individuo.
Me preguntaron que de donde venía.
Contesté que sí, que no tenía planes determinados,
Contesté que no, que de ahí en adelante.
Bien.
Tomé entonces un trozo de piedra que encontré en un río
Y empecé a trabajar con ella,
Empecé a pulirla,
De ella hice una parte de mi propia vida.
Pero esto es demasiado largo.
Corté unos árboles para navegar,
Buscaba peces,
Buscaba diferentes cosas
(Yo soy el Individuo.)
Hasta que me empecé a aburrir nuevamente.
Las tempestades aburren,
Los truenos, los relámpagos,
Yo soy el Individuo.
Bien. Me puse a pensar un poco,
Preguntas estúpidas se me venían a la cabeza,
Falsos problemas.
Entonces empecé a vagar por unos bosques.
Llegué a un árbol y a otro árbol,

Llegué a una fuente,
A una fosa en que se véian algunas ratas:
Aquí vengo yo, dije entonces,
¿Habéis visto por aquí una tribu,
Un pueblo salvaje que hace fuego?
De este modo me desplacé hacia el oeste
Acompañado por ostros seres,
O más bien solo.
Para ver hay que creer, me decían,
Yo soy el Individuo.
Formas veía en la oscuridad,
Nubes tal vez,
Tal vez veía nubes, veía relámpagos,
A todo esto habían pasado ya varios días,
Yo me sentía morir;
Inventé unas máquinas
Construí relojes,
Armas, vehículos,
Yo soy el Individuo.
Apenas tenía tiempo para enterrar a mis muertos,
Apenas tenía tiempo para sembrar,
Yo soy el Individuo.
Años más tarde concebí unas cosas,
Unas formas,
Crucé las fronteras
Y permanecí fijo en una especie de nicho,
En una barca que navegó cuarenta días,
Cuarenta noches,
Yo soy el Individuo.
Luego vinieron unas sequías,
Vinieron unas guerras,
Tipos de color entraron al valle,
Pero yo debía seguir adelante,
Debía producir.
Produje ciencia, verdades inmutables,
Produje tanagras,
Di a luz libros de miles de páginas,
Se me hinchó la cara,
Construí un fonógrafo,

La máquina de coser,
Empezaron a aparecer los primeros automóviles,
Yo soy el Individuo.
Alguien segregaba planetas,
¡Arboles segregaba!
Pero yo segregaba herramientas,
Muebles, útiles de escritorio,
Yo soy el Individuo.
Se construyeron también ciudades,
Rutas,
Instituciones religiosas pasaron de moda,
Buscaban dicha, buscaban felicidad,
Yo soy el Individuo.
Después me dediqué mejor a viajar,
A practicar, a practicar idiomas,
Idiomas,
Yo soy el Individuo.
Miré por una cerradura,
Sí, miré, qué digo, miré,
Para salir de la duda miré,
Detrás de unas cortinas,
Yo soy el Individuo.
Bien.
Mejor es tal vez que vuelva a ese valle,
A esa roca que me sirvió de hogar,
Y empiece a grabar de nuevo,
De atrás para adelante grabar
El mundo al revés.
Pero no: la vida no tiene sentido.

IDA VITALE

Born in Montevideo in 1919, Ida Vitale has had poems published
in newspapers, magazines and anthologies.

Canon

Everything has already been said
and a resplendence of centuries
defends it from its echo.
How shall I celebrate the mingled perfume of the night,
the autumn growing in my side,
friendship, occupations,
today's day,
beautiful and dead for always,
or the calm birds of sunset?
How tell of love,
its indomitable, daily return,
when many, so many times
have been frozen by words, by dawns?
How enclose it in a figure
that is new, extreme and my own,
beneath a name as yet overlooked,
but unique and necessary?
So would I covet total innocence,
as in the rose,
which comes with its odor and its scintillations,
its repetitious, sleeping dews,
from the center of gardens turned to dust
and rises eternally
renewed.

Canon

Ya todo ha sido dicho
y un resplandor de siglos
lo defiende del eco.
¿Cómo cantar el confuso perfume de la noche,
el otoño creciendo en mi costado,
la amistad, los oficios,
el día de hoy,
hermoso y muerto para siempre,
o los pájaros calmos de los atardeceres?
¿Cómo decir de amor,
su indomable regreso cotidiano,
si a tantos, tantas veces,
han helado papeles, madrugadas?
¿Cómo encerrarlo en una cifra
nueva, extrema y mía,
bajo un nombre hasta ahora inadvertido,
y único y necesario?
Tanto haría falta la inocencia total,
como en la rosa,
que viene con su olor y sus destellos,
sus dormidos rocíos repetidos,
del centro de jardines vueltos polvo
ye de nuevo innumerablemente
levantados.

ENRIQUE LIHN

Two volumes of poetry and a collection of essays represent the published work of this young Chilean, born in Santiago in 1929.

Newly Born

I

I must be brief; I am
about to be born—time runs down me
like a shudder—
horrible,
I am losing my dream creeping, trying.

II

Newly born,
from one grave to another grave
I slip, I am flung. . . .

III

Today they will baptize me.
What name can they give
me since I am
agreeable to everything?

IV

If I could choose
I would melt away. . . .

Recién nacido

I

Debo ser breve: estoy
a punto de nacer—el tiempo me recorre
como un escalofrio—
horror,
pierdo mi sueño a gatas, en tanteos.

II

Recién nacido,
de una fosa a otra fosa
me escurro, soy lanzado. . . .

III

Hoy me bautizarán,
¿qué nombre pueden
ponerme a mí que estoy
dispuesto a todo?

IV

Si pudiese elegir
me esfumaría. . . .